Handcuff Blues

Handcuff Blues

Publisher's Cataloging-In-Publication

Johnson, Toni (Toni Elizabeth)
    Handcuff blues. Volume 1, Crime doesn't pay : Helping teens stay out of trouble with the law / Toni Johnson ; illustrations by Daerick Gross Sr. -- 1st. ed.
    p. cm.

Includes index.

    SUMMARY: Twelve stories about young people who committed crimes, ranging from shoplifting and drunk driving to vandalism and manslaughter. Through the eyes of these teens, you see how the law works and the choices they have to make about their futures.

    Preassigned LCCN: 98-87133   ISBN: 1-885535-43-0

    1. Juvenile delinquency--United States--Juvenile literature. 2. Juvenile justice, Administration of--United States --Juvenile literature. I. Title.

HV9069.J64 1999   364.36
                             QBI98--1286

www.handcuffblues.com

Goofy Foot Press
P.O Box 69365
West Hollywood, CA 90069-0365
phone (310) 659-8430
fax (310) 652-2995

Handcuff Blues

Helping Teens Stay Out Of Trouble With The Law

Volume 1
Crime Doesn't Pay

by

Toni E. Johnson, J.D.

Illustrations by Daerick Gross Sr.

Inside Handcuff Blues

1. Bianca
page 1

A prom to remember.

2. Wesley & Franco
page 13

Simple mischief or
assault with a deadly weapon?

3. Scott
page 27

Leaving a message for Billy.

4. Becky
page 49

After a *fun* day of shoplifting.

5. Justin & Brad
page 65

A day at the beach
goes bad.

6. Cheryl
page 75

Cheating to get into college.

7. Jenny
page 89

Jenny suspected her boyfriend might be doing something illegal.

8. Jimmy
page 105

Three strikes, you're out.

9. Anthony
page 119

Finally, jumped into the gang.

10. Marty
page 129

Before the crash.

11. Kevin
page 139

"Fun" at the big house.

12. Gary
page 159

"I was just doing my job."

Resources	page 167
Glossary Of Legal Terms	page 181
Index	page 199

I am a criminal defense lawyer. My job is to help people who are in trouble with the law. That's why I have written this book. It's about teenagers and young adults who found themselves in serious trouble.

These stories are about real people. I have changed their names and many of the details to protect their identities, but they are people who are a lot more like you than you might want to believe. Unfortunately, they didn't think about the consequences of their actions.

In most states, you can be tried as an adult by the age of sixteen. In some states, it's even younger. By then you can get into serious trouble that will follow you or haunt you for the rest of your life. All because you might not have thought about the impact of your actions.

From having worked with hundreds of kids like you, I simply ask that you take a moment to think. I hope that you will never have to walk through the police stations, courts and prisons—a walk that many teenagers and adults find to be full of fear and humiliation.

Chapter 1
Bianca

Bianca and her friends were so excited about their high school prom that they talked about nothing else. They discussed how they were going to wear their hair, the kind of music the band would be playing, and every other detail you could possibly imagine.

All of the students had to go to the prom on special buses that would pick them up at the high school. That's because there had been problems with drinking and driving in the past. Since Bianca's house was so close to the school, she, her friend Kathy, and their dates decided to meet there beforehand.

When the big night finally arrived, Bianca's friends came to her house nearly two hours early. Bianca's parents greeted everyone, took a few hundred photographs, and then left.

"Where are your parents going?" Frank asked.

"They're going to my grandfather's seventy-fifth birthday party," she explained.

"He's an old dude," Frank said.

As soon as Bianca's parents had driven away, Jay shouted, "I've got a surprise in my car!"

The four friends opened the garage door and walked out to Jay's car. A twelve-pack of beer was in the trunk.

"My older brother got it for us."

They went to the backyard and sat down on the patio chairs, where they started sipping beers and talking.

Mrs. Monahan lived across the street from Bianca's family. She had been in her front yard weeding when she saw Jay take the beers out of the trunk. A few minutes later she saw Bianca and Jay walk to the car and grab more beers. She shook her head with disapproval and continued her gardening.

As she was finishing her weeding, Mrs. Monahan heard laughter coming from Bianca's house. She then saw the kids getting into Bianca's car. When Bianca got behind the wheel, Mrs. Monahan became very concerned. She called to Bianca as the car backed out of the driveway.

"Wait. Wait. I can drive you!" but the music in the car was turned up too loud for anyone to hear.

Jay popped open a couple of beers and handed one to Kathy.

"Frank, how you doin'?"

"Don't need one, dude," Frank said, holding up his open beer.

As she was driving away, Bianca saw Mrs. Monahan waving her arms, so she waved back. She had driven about three blocks when she noticed a police car was behind her. This made Bianca nervous. She pulled up to a stop sign and put on her right blinker. While trying to make the turn, she drove over the curb. The police officer immediately put on his lights.

Bianca pulled over and took a deep breath. The officer approached her window.

"I'll need to see your license and registration."

Bianca handed him her license.

"The registration is in the glove box."

"Go ahead and take it out," the officer said. "Have you been drinking? I smell alcohol on your breath."

"No, officer," Bianca said.

"Step out of the car, miss."

Bianca stumbled a little as she tried to stand up.

"I want you to perform some Field Sobriety Tests. These will help me determine if you're intoxicated. Now, stand up straight, put your head back, your arms out and close your eyes. Bring your index finger to the tip of your nose."

The officer demonstrated what he wanted Bianca to do.

"Okay, keep your eyes closed."

Bianca tried to follow his instructions, but when she closed her eyes she started swaying back and forth. She brought her finger towards her nose, but it landed on her cheek.

Bianca tried to touch her nose again, this time with even less success.

"Okay. That's enough," the officer said. "See the white line painted on the edge of the street?"

"Yes."

"I want you to walk along the line, placing one foot directly in front of the other. You should take off your high heels first."

Bianca sat down in the driver's seat and removed her shoes. She stood on the line in her stocking feet.

"Place one foot in front of the other," the officer directed.

Bianca took two steps, lost her balance and stepped off the line.

"Can I try again?"

"Sure."

This time, she took three steps before she stepped off the line.

"I think that's enough. Bianca, I'm placing you under arrest for Driving Under the Influence."

"But you don't understand. I'm going to my prom. I was only going about six or seven blocks to the school. Please don't arrest me," she pleaded.

"In six or seven blocks you could have hurt or killed someone. Besides, you're under age and you shouldn't be drinking anyway. I'm going to read you your rights."

The officer pulled a small card from his pocket and started reading it to Bianca. He then placed Bianca in the squad car and walked back to where the others were.

"Have all of you been drinking?"

Three sets of very wide eyes looked back at him.

"Well?"

"Yes sir," Jay said.

"I want you to perform some Field Sobriety Tests. These will help me determine if you're intoxicated."

The officer peered into the car. He could see three open cans of beer.

"Stay put. Don't get out of the car."

He grabbed his radio and called for backup. Within ten minutes, another police car pulled up.

"You three, step out of the car."

"What's your name?" the officer asked Kathy.

"Kathy Uslefski."

"Do you have identification?"

"In my purse."

"Take it out for me."

Kathy handed him her I.D. She noticed that another officer was talking to the guys, looking at their I.D.s. Kathy was escorted to the squad car and placed in the backseat with Bianca.

"Why am I in trouble?" she asked. "I was just a passenger."

"You're under twenty-one. It's against the law for you to be drinking. It doesn't matter if you are driving a car, walking on the sidewalk or sitting in your own backyard."

"Where are you taking us?" Bianca asked.

"To the police station, then we'll contact your parents."

"But we're going to miss the prom," Kathy moaned.

"Missing the prom is the least of your worries right now," the officer said.

They were taken to the police station and booked into custody. Bianca was given the choice of taking a breathalyzer test, a urine test, or a blood test to determine how much she had been drinking. She chose the breathalyzer test. It showed that her alcohol level was three times the legal limit.

When Bianca's parents arrived at the police station the desk sergeant explained that Bianca had been charged with Driving Under the Influence.

"Her blood alcohol level was .12%, which is way above the legal limit. We'll release her to you in a few minutes."

Her dad asked the sergeant if they could keep Bianca overnight.

"It's a lesson I don't think she'll forget."

"We'll keep her tonight and release her to you in the morning, but she's pretty scared."

Bianca watched as Kathy, Jay and Frank went home with their parents. She sat in the cell and waited.

Later, the sergeant came to her cell.

"Your parents have asked us to keep you overnight— to teach you a lesson."

Tears rolled down Bianca's cheeks and onto her prom dress. When she was finally released the next morning her parents were waiting.

"You're grounded for the rest of your life," her mother said.

Bianca's father looked sad.

"You can't even begin to understand how disappointed we are in you."

Her parents made an appointment to meet with an attorney. He listened to Bianca's story.

"There isn't much I can do if your alcohol level was as high as you say. If you enter a guilty plea to the D.U.I., the Judge will make you complete a sixteen-week alcohol program, you'll have to pay a fine of $300 and do one-hundred hours of community service. You'll lose your license until you are twenty-one, and you'll be placed on probation for five years."

When she got home, Bianca immediately called Kathy.

"My attorney says I'm gonna lose my license until I'm twenty-one. My parents are really upset. The police impounded my car and my dad can't get it for two weeks. By then the storage fees will be over $400. What did they charge you with?"

"Something like Possession of Alcohol in a Vehicle," Kathy said. "I got a fine and can't get my license until I'm eighteen."

"What about Frank?"

"Frank got a fine and his license will probably be suspended until he's forty because of his prior tickets. What happened to Jay?"

"He got the same as you and Frank. His parents are really mad. They're sending him to a military school. He even has to stay there over the summer."

"Some prom night, huh?"

"Yeah. One to remember."

The Law

DRIVING UNDER THE INFLUENCE OF ALCOHOL
OR DRUGS
Vehicle Code Section 45

Any person under the age of 21-years who drives with a blood alcohol level of .04% is in violation of Vehicle Code Section 45.

A violation of Vehicle Code Section 45 is punishable by 2 days in the county jail or 100 hours of community service, a fine of up to$1,500, participation in a 16-week alcohol rehabilitation program, loss of driving privileges until the age of 21, and probation for a term of 7 years.

POSSESSION OF ALCOHOL IN A VEHICLE BY PERSONS
UNDER 21 YEARS
Vehicle Code Section 67

No passenger in a motor vehicle under the age of 21 years shall knowingly possess an alcoholic beverage.

A violation of Vehicle Code section 67 is punishable by a fine up to $400, participation in a 10-week alcohol rehabilitation program, loss of driving privileges for 2 years and probation for a term of 4 years.

Since the laws in each state are different, the laws cited
in this book may not reflect those in your state.

Questions

1. Is the legal limit for intoxication different for minors than for adults?

The limit is usually much lower for minors than for adults. In the state where Bianca lives, the legal limit for adults is .08%. However, for minors the legal limit is .04%. Also, the penalties for minors are more severe. For a first time offense, Bianca lost her license until she turns 21-years-old. An adult would have lost his or her license for 6 months. The reason why a minor receives a harsher sentence is because the minor has violated two laws — driving while intoxicated and drinking alcohol while a minor.

2. Kathy, Jay and Frank weren't driving. Why were their driving privileges suspended?

Even if they weren't driving, a minor caught with alcohol or drugs will often have his or her driver's license suspended.

3. What if Bianca had refused to take the Field Sobriety Tests?

If she had refused to take the test, she would have automatically been transported to the police station to take a blood, urine or breath test.

4. What if she refused to take the required blood, urine or breath test?

The law would automatically assume that she was guilty of Driving Under the Influence.

Chapter 2
Wesley & Franco

Wesley and Franco spent much of their summer vacation in front of the television watching movies and playing video games. In the evenings, they would walk to the local market and buy sodas.

One night they stopped on an overpass to watch the traffic go by. The temptation was just too great. Franco took his soda and tried to pour it onto the hoods of the passing vehicles. Most of the time he missed.

"You gotta time it just right," he said to Wesley. "Come on, you try."

Wesley followed Franco's example. He managed to hit the trunks of several cars. Then he stopped.

"Let's go. I don't wanna waste any more of my soda."

The next night they returned to the overpass with several plastic bottles filled with water.

"You gotta start pouring as soon at the car goes under the pass," Franco said. "Otherwise you miss."

Soon they became proficient at hitting the windshields. "We haven't seen rain in months. These guys must be wondering where all the water's coming from," Wesley laughed.

After a few more evenings of dumping water onto cars, they decided to try a new concoction. They put ketchup, mustard, food coloring, dirt and anything else that looked messy into the bottles. Then they added some water.

Franco missed the first car that went by. The mixture splattered onto the pavement. He concentrated on the next car and was rewarded with a direct hit. The car swerved and slammed on its brakes, but kept going. The boys hid below the railing, laughing.

"My turn!" Wesley yelled.

Wesley's first attempt hit the back windshield. The brake lights went on and the car slowed. The boys peeked over the rail to see if it had stopped.

"All clear. That was so cool! Let's try it again."

As the next car passed under the concrete structure Wesley dumped out a huge amount of the goop. It hit the windshield and the roof with a thud. The driver stopped on the shoulder of the road. He got out of his car and surveyed the mess. Then he took out a flashlight and shined it at the overpass. The boys could barely contain their laughter.

"What if he spots us?"

"We'll run. He's too far away to catch us. Besides he's old, and it's too dark for him to see us."

The man scratched his head and then drove off. The boys left on their bikes laughing and joking about their successful night's work.

"We should try our luck at a different overpass tomorrow," Franco said. "Just in case someone calls the police."

"Let's try something different next time," Wesley replied.

The boys laughed hysterically. "We nearly gave her a heart attack!"

"Like what?"

"How about some rocks? Just small ones."

"I like that idea."

The next night, the boys filled plastic grocery bags with dirt clods and small rocks and rode to a different overpass. Wesley took out a dirt clod and dropped it on a passing car. It hit the roof with a loud bang. The driver quickly pulled over.

"Oh, man. We better get out of here."

The boys took off running. After several blocks they threw themselves on some grass to catch their breath.

"Did you hear the sound it made? Must've put a good-sized dent in the roof."

"Yeah. Should we try it again?"

"Sure! But let's wait a couple of nights," Wesley said.

A few nights passed, and the boys decided it was safe to try again. They took their bag of ammunition and headed for an overpass.

Wesley grabbed a small dirt clod with each hand.

"Double trouble," he yelled, dropping the clods in unison.

The clods hit the car squarely on its windshield. Dust and gravel flew everywhere as the car fishtailed and came to a stop. An older woman stepped out. She was shaken and held onto the car to support herself. The boys laughed hysterically, covering their mouths to keep from being heard. In a few minutes, the woman got into the car and drove off.

"We nearly gave her a heart attack!" Wesley laughed.

For the next few weeks, Wesley and Franco continued their "bomb drops." The more erratic a car's response after being hit, the more they enjoyed it.

One night, as they reached their favorite overpass, Wesley came up with yet another new idea.

"Let's try dropping together to see who's the better shot."

Both boys took a good-sized clod and leaned over the railing.

"Ready, set, drop."

Both clods hit the windshield. The driver slammed on the brakes, sending her car into a spin. It came to a rest on the side of the road facing the overpass. The boys were so entranced by the spin they forgot to duck. The driver, a young woman by the name of Maggie Landowski, leapt out of the car.

"Hey you little twerps, get down here!"

Both boys turned to run. The woman ran up the slope next to the overpass and the chase was on.

"She's catching up with us," Wesley whimpered.

"Keep running, she won't catch us. She's a girl."

When Maggie started gaining on them, the boys split up in different directions. Maggie followed the slower of the two. She yelled at him to stop, but he kept running. When she got close enough, she shoved him as hard as she could. Wesley went flying on his stomach.

When he stopped, Maggie jammed her knee between his shoulder blades.

"Get off me!" Wesley gasped.

"Don't move, you little punk, or I'll punch your lights out. You almost killed me, you stupid brat."

Maggie reached into her jacket and pulled out a small cellular phone. She dialed 911 while Wesley squirmed beneath her.

"Operator? I'm on the corner of Jefferson and Winton. Two boys hit my car with rocks, and I've got one of them pinned to the ground."

Wesley struggled to get free. Maggie grabbed him by his hair and yanked.

"If you don't send the police soon, there's no telling what I'll do with him!"

Two minutes later, a squad car arrived. One of the officers picked Wesley up and put him in the backseat. The other took a report from Maggie.

"You said there was a second boy?"

"He ran off the other way."

The officer turned to Wesley, "What's your friend's name?"

"I don't know what you're talking about," Wesley said defiantly.

"You know what? Don't tell us his name. We'll only charge you. Your friend goes free while you sit in jail, and you'll probably be there for a long time."

Wesley remained silent. Soon, another police car pulled up. They put Wesley in the back and drove away.

"Are they taking him to jail?" Maggie asked.

"Yeah. We've had a rash of these incidents over the last couple of weeks. We're going to cruise the area to see if we can spot the other boy. We'd like you to come with us, to help identify him."

Maggie and the officers got into the squad car. About thirty minutes later, she spotted a boy walking down one of the streets.

"That's him!" she roared.

When Franco saw the police car, he started to run. The officers chased him on foot.

"Stop! Police!" they yelled.

One of the officers caught up to Franco and grabbed him from behind. He shoved Franco against a wall while the other officer pulled out his flashlight and pointed it in Franco's face.

"Why'd you run?"

"I was scared." Franco's body was shaking.

"You were scared, huh? Of what? Maybe you were doin' something you weren't supposed to be doin'?"

They escorted Franco to the car.

"Mam, do you recognize this boy?"

"Yes. He was one of the boys up on the overpass."

"I wasn't there! I didn't do anything!" Franco pleaded.

The officer spoke in his sternest voice, "We've already caught your friend. He told us all about you. Said you were the one who threw the rocks, and he just watched."

Franco turned red, "That little liar! He threw just as many as I did!"

The officer winked at Maggie, "I think we've got both of them now. Thank you for your help."

At the urging of their parents, the boys told the police the truth about what they had done. Both were detained at juvenile hall. The Judge hearing their case refused to let them go home.

"You're a threat to the safety of others," he said.

A total of fifteen cars had been damaged. As a result, Wesley and Franco were charged with fifteen counts of Assault With a Deadly Weapon and fifteen counts of Throwing An Object at a Vehicle.

Wesley's attorney explained that the objects the boys dropped were considered deadly weapons because they could have resulted in someone being killed.

At their next court appearance, the Prosecutor barked at the boys, "Your behavior was despicable. It was only by luck that no one was badly injured. The only reason you're not being charged as adults is because of your age. If either of you were one year older, I'd make sure that you were charged in adult court."

Before trial, both boys were offered a camp commitment. This means that instead of being placed in a prison for juvenile offenders, the boys would live at a boot camp type of program for three to four months.

While the boys' parents weren't happy with their sons' behavior, they felt that this was too harsh of a punishment. After all, it was just a childish prank, and no one had been hurt. They encouraged the boys to reject the offer.

The offer was rejected and a trial was held. Because Wesley and Franco were minors, they were not entitled to a jury. Their cases were heard by a Judge. After the victims had testified and the defense had put on its witnesses, the Judge found the boys guilty of all thirty charges. He sentenced each of the boys to a long term camp commitment.

"If they behave themselves, they should be out in a year," he said.

The Judge also ordered the boys' parents to pay the victims for their damages.

"Full restitution is ordered to be paid by the parents to all victims."

"May I speak, your honor?" Franco's father asked?

"Go ahead."

"My son, Franco, he's a good boy. What he did was stupid, but he didn't mean any harm. Sending him away from his family for a year is unfair. Besides, before the trial he was offered only three or four months in boot camp."

The Judge glared and nearly began to snarle.

"You think I'm being unfair? People could have been killed because of your son's behavior. Your son didn't do this just one night, he did it over and over. He had plenty of time to think about his actions, but that didn't stop him."

"You think I'm being too harsh? The only reason I didn't send these boys to adult court is because they are still thirteen."

"Furthermore, where were you and your wife when all of this was going on? What was your son doing running around at night unsupervised? I think you should take a hard look at yourself before you start pointing a finger at me. If I had the authority to put you in jail for your lack of parenting skills I would. Unfortunately, I don't. As long as you continue to make excuses for your son and allow his bad behavior, he will end up right back here in my court room, and next time the sentence won't be so light."

"Madame Clerk, I want to add to my order. Both sets of parents are to attend parenting classes. Proof of completion of the class must be filed with this court within sixty days. Court is adjourned."

In addition to the criminal cases, the people whose vehicles had been damaged by the rocks filed civil lawsuits against the parents of Wesley and Franco. They sued to recover medical costs for their injuries and the emotional distress caused by the trauma.

The parents ended up paying more than $65,000, plus another $20,000 in attorneys fees.

The Law

THROWING OBJECTS AT A VEHICLE
Criminal Statute Section 11378.5

Any person who unlawfully throws, hurls or projects at a vehicle while the vehicle is in motion or stationary any rock, stone, brick, bottle, piece of wood or metal or any item and causes more than $500 damage to the vehicle is guilty of a felony and is punishable by imprisonment in a state prison for 2, 4 or 6 years.

ASSAULT WITH A DEADLY WEAPON
Criminal Statute Section 776.3

Any person who unlawfully commits an assault upon the person of another with a deadly weapon or instrument other than a firearm or by means likely to produce great bodily injury shall be punished by imprisonment in a state prison for 2, 3 or 4 years.

RESTITUTION
Criminal Statute Section 1100

When a minor is convicted of violating statute 11378.5 and the minor is unable to pay the restitution, the parent of the minor will be liable for payment.

Since the laws in each state are different, the laws cited in this book may not reflect those in your state.

Questions

1. What is restitution?

Restitution is when a judge orders a defendant to repay the victim for damages caused during the commission of a crime.

In some states, a minor's family can be ordered to pay for the damage done by their child, as was the case for Wesley and Franco's families.

2. Are teenagers always tried in a juvenile delinquency court when they are accused of committing a crime?

Most states have separate courts for minors who have been accused of committing a crime. However, under some conditions, a minor can be tried in an adult court. There are examples of this in other chapters of this book

3. What kind of sentences are available in juvenile cases?

In giving a sentence, the court will usually assign certain terms and conditions that the minor must abide by. These might include attending school, getting a job, attending drug rehabilitation classes, or the following:

HOME ON PROBATION — For a first time offender with a less serious case, the Judge might consider a sentence of home on probation. The minor must obey his or her parent or guardian, abide by a curfew and follow any other conditions imposed by the Judge.

COMMUNITY SERVICE/HARD LABOR — The Judge may sentence a minor to community service or hard labor, usually graffiti removal or trash cleanup.

JUVENILE HALL/JUVENILE DETENTION CENTER — Juvenile hall is a detention center for juveniles which is run by the county. The Judge can place a minor in juvenile hall where he or she will attend school, and cannot leave the hall until the sentence is completed. This is usually for a short term.

PLACEMENT IN A FOSTER HOME OR FACILITY — The Judge can place a minor in a foster home if the parents are unable to provide proper care or discipline, or the minor can be placed in a county facility. These are set up to house minors who need a more controlled environment than they have at home.

BOOT CAMP — Camp is a highly disciplined, almost military-like facility where minors live for the length of their sentence. They are usually located in rural areas. The focus is on hard work, discipline and schooling.

PRISON FOR YOUTHFUL OFFENDERS — The final option for a Judge is to place a minor in a prison for youthful offenders. Prison for youthful offenders is only used when the crime is violent or serious, when other options have failed, or when the Judge believes the minor must be incarcerated to protect the community.

Chapter 3
Scott

Scott and Billy lived in nice neighborhoods with nice homes and nice cars. They went to the same school, but hung out with different groups of guys.

Scott's former girlfriend had dumped him to be with Billy. It enraged Scott every time he saw the two of them together, especially since Billy liked to flaunt his new relationship. Whenever he saw Scott, Billy would pull his girlfriend close and kiss her, then look at Scott and laugh. The hostilities between Billy and Scott had spread to their respective friends. They clashed all of the time.

A day before Spring break, one of Scott's friends told him, "My mom is friends with Billy's mom. She says they're going out of town for vacation."

"Maybe we should check out their house while they're gone," Scott replied.

"Yeah. We could leave Billy a message."

"My thought exactly, dude."

A few days after Billy and his family left for vacation, Hank, Scott and some of their friends went over to Billy's house. They broke a window in the back and crawled inside. After tearing around the house, they met in the kitchen.

"Anything to eat in here?" Scott asked while opening the refrigerator. "Hey, they didn't leave us anything."

"Maybe no food, but look what I found!" said Hank, holding several bottles of liquor. "They left liquor in the cabinet just for us."

The boys turned on the television in the family room, put their feet up and passed around the bottles. The more they drank, the louder they became. One of them knocked over a lamp.

"Don't worry about it. Billy deserves to have his house messed up. He's a loser. Let's show him what we think of him."

"Yeah. Let's show Billy who's the boss."

Hank took a knife out of the drawer and began shredding the furniture, ripping big slashes in the fabric, then pulling out the stuffing.

"Look. I found some spray paint," Scott yelled, throwing one of the cans to Jared. They ran through the house tagging the walls.

Jared picked up a chair and hit the wall with it, making a big gash in the wallboard. He pulled chunks of the wallboard away, leaving a huge gaping hole. He then turned to the doors, kicking holes in them. Aaron found a baseball bat and hit a home run into the television set.

By the time they were done, the boys had ruined every piece of furniture in the house. They poured swimming pool chlorine over all the carpets and on all of the family's clothes. They turned over the refrigerator, letting it fall into the counter top.

Eventually, they stopped to admire the destruction around them.

"Let's leave Billy a little message."

"Good work, boys. Job well done. Let's pick up some booze and split," Scott said.

As they walked out the back door, Hank stopped.

"We forgot something."

He ran upstairs to the bathroom, turned on the water in the bathtub full blast, closed the drain and ran back down.

"Now the place will be clean when they get home."

A week later, Billy and his parents pulled in the driveway, home from their vacation. Jeanine Hubbard turned to her husband Randy and said, "That's strange, water's coming from under the garage door."

"Might be a leak in a pipe. I'm sure it's nothing serious," Randy said. "Billy, help your mother carry the bags into the house and I'll check it out."

Randy took the padlock off the garage door. Before he could open it, he heard his wife cry out. He ran into the house. Water poured down the steps and out the front door. All of the furniture had been ruined, there were holes in all of the walls, garbage floated in the water, nothing was left untouched.

Randy stood silently, looking at the disaster his house had become. Jeanine began to cry.

Randy walked to the kitchen to call the police, but the phone was nowhere to be found. He checked upstairs, but couldn't find a working phone. He walked out to the garage to use the phone he had there to call the police.

Ten minutes later, two officers arrived.

"Geez, I've never seen anything like this. Everything's ruined!" one officer muttered to the other.

The two policeman called for an investigation team. An officer arrived with a camera and began taking pictures of the damage. A detective was also assigned to the case.

Detective Reynolds surveyed the damage and then questioned the Hubbards.

"Any idea who did this?"

Jeanine and Randy shook their heads.

"Anyone angry with you?"

"Nope."

"I've never seen anything like this," he said, shaking his head. "Have you got a place where you can stay?"

"I guess we'll go to a hotel," Randy said. "Why would anyone do this?"

"I think I know," Billy said.

"What?" inquired Detective Reynolds.

"I noticed there was some graffiti on the wall in the living room. One of the words is the nickname for Scott. I think Hank wrote his name too."

"Who are Scott and Hank?" the Detective asked.

"They're a couple of guys I go to school with. I've had some trouble with them this year."

Officers were dispatched to pick up the boys. Once Scott and Hank were at the station, Detective Reynolds began the interview process.

Scott sat in one room with his parents. Detective Reynolds explained to them what had happened to the Hubbard's home. He read Scott his constitutional rights and Scott agreed to talk to him.

The detective said that some of the graffiti had been identified as Scott's. At first, Scott denied having any knowledge about the damage.

"We've got a fingerprint team at the house. They've found lots of fresh prints. But I'm sure none of them are yours."

Scott gulped, and then admitted that maybe he had been at the house with a few of his friends.

"We partied a little, but didn't do any damage."

"Then who wrote the graffiti on the walls?"

"Must've been one of the other guys."

"You're telling me you had nothing to do with the damage that was done?" the detective asked.

"I didn't do anything. I saw the other guys messin' the place up, but I told them to stop."

"Why didn't you call the police, or tell your parents what had happened?"

"Guess I was too scared."

"Scott, if you're lying, it's only going to get worse for you. Tell me the truth now and I can help you, but if you keep lying, I can't help you."

"How much damage was done?" Scott's mother asked.

"I don't know exactly. The insurance adjuster will be out tomorrow, but it's bad. More than $100,000. There isn't a room in the house that was left undamaged."

Scott's mother gasped.

"Why don't you sit here for awhile and try to remember exactly what happened," Detective Reynolds said to Scott.

The Detective went into the other room with Hank and his mother. He introduced himself and explained why Hank had been brought to the station. He read Hank his rights.

"If you had anything to do with this, you tell the detective!" Hank's mother growled. "Jeanine Hubbard and I have been friends for years. She treated you like one of her own. You better start talking right now. Jail will be nothing compared to what I'll do to you."

Hank looked at his mother, then down at the table.

"Okay. I was involved, but I didn't do very much."

"So you were involved in the vandalism?"

"Sort of, but Aaron and Scott did most of the damage. Scott's the one who broke the window. He and Aaron trashed the place. I watched, but I didn't damage anything."

Detective Reynolds returned to the interview room where Scott and his parents were waiting.

"I just finished interviewing your friend Hank. He tells a different story. According to Hank, you were the one who broke the window so all of you could get into the house. Fortunately, we found some blood on the glass left in the frame. We can do a DNA test on it to see if it matches yours. I notice you have a cut on your hand. Do you think the blood on the window might match with yours?"

"Well, I did break the window, but I didn't do anything else."

"Did you take anything?"

"We didn't take any of their stuff."

"I guess there wasn't much to take after you got through. Did you take any liquor?"

"Yeah. We took a few bottles."

"Scott, I'm going to be real honest with you because I want to help you. I think you were involved with trashing the Hubbard's house. If you want me to help you, you're going to have to tell me the truth."

Scott looked at this parents. His dad nodded.

"Tell him what you know, son."

"I was sort of involved."

Scott went on to describe what he and the others had done. The Detective recorded everything he said.

Although Scott had only turned sixteen a few weeks before, Detective Reynolds had him booked as an adult. This meant he was taken to an adult jail with serious adult offenders. It also meant he could be sentenced to do time in state prison.

Hank, who was still fifteen, was transported to the juvenile detention center for booking. He was detained for several days and then brought to court. The charges against him were read.

"You are charged in Case Number J56329K with the following offenses: Count 1, violation of Criminal Code Section 776.3, Vandalism, a felony; Count 2, violation of Criminal Code Section 778, Defacement of Personal Property of Another, a felony; Count 3, violation of Criminal Code Section 324, First Degree Burglary, a felony. How do you plead?"

Hank's attorney leaned over and whispered.

"Say not guilty."

"Not guilty," Hank said.

Hank's attorney, Mr. Angelino, spoke up.

"Your Honor, I'd like to be heard on the issue of the minor's release to his parents."

The D.A. protested, "Your Honor, the minor was involved in literally destroying a home. The boys did in excess of $150,000 damage. They damaged every room in the house. They tore holes in the walls, dumped bleach on the victim's clothing and on all of the carpets. They slashed and ruined every piece of furniture. They intentionally left the water running in the upstairs bathroom. The Hubbards were on vacation and the water flooded the house for several days before they returned. Judge, they completely destroyed these people's home. These boys are a danger to the community. Releasing them to their parents would put the Hubbards at risk."

"I can appreciate the D.A.'s position, but I believe she is overstating the viciousness of the boys. My client has no previous record. He is a very good student. His parents are here today and can vouch for his good behavior at home. Keeping my client in juvenile detention until the trial would prove to be detrimental to his well-being."

The Judge turned to Hank.

"I'm not releasing you from custody. You have been accused of committing a horrible crime. You invaded the sanctity of someone's home, and demolished it. You showed complete callousness towards the property of others. It boggles my mind that you could do this. You can sit in juvenile hall."

A few days later, Hank's attorney went to see the D.A. He spoke about a possible plea agreement.

"Can your minor's parents pay restitution?" the D.A. asked.

"They have some money, but not $44,000, which is Hank's share of the damage. They can pay about $5,000 right now."

"I think your client deserves to go to prison for youthful offenders, but if his parents come up with full restitution for the victims, I'll reconsider."

A month later, Mr. Angelino met with the D.A. again.

"Hank's parents have sold their home and one of their cars. When the sale of the home is completed, they will have $35,000 to pay towards restitution."

The D.A. nodded. "Your client pleads to all three counts. He will be sentenced to a long term camp commitment of one year. The court will order repayment of the balance owing on the restitution. In addition, the minor will participate in a mediation session with the victims."

Mr. Angelino met with Hank and his parents to explain the D.A.'s offer.

"What's camp?" they asked.

"Camp is a facility for minors that's run by the probation department. It's like being in boot camp. It focuses on hard work, discipline and education."

"What if we don't accept the deal?"

"If we go to trial and lose, Hank could be sent to a prison for juvenile delinquents, where he would be locked up in a cell with kids who have committed violent crimes. It's a pretty harsh place."

Hank agreed to the D.A.'s offer.

A probation officer made the arrangements for the Hubbards to confront Hank. When they arrived for the mediation session, Jeanine glared at Hank.

"I know your parents. Your mother and I are good friends. I've known you since you were a baby. How could you come into my house and wreck it? Didn't it bother you that you knew us? You've been a guest in our house. Why would you do this?"

Hank looked at his feet. The probation officer reminded Hank that part of his sentence requires him to take responsibility for his acts.

"Unless you do so, we'll call this off right now."

Hank remained quiet for a moment. "I made a mistake. I let myself get carried away. I think about how nice you were to me when I was small, and I feel really bad. I wish I could take back what I did. I can't believe how stupid I was. I don't know if you'd let me, but after I get out, I'd like to come over and do anything I can to help."

"Hank, I never want you near our house again. When I look at you, I'll remember the horror I felt when I saw our house and what you'd done to it. I don't want to live in the house anymore."

The session went on for two hours. When the Hubbards left they felt drained, but they'd had their say. The probation officer explained that it usually helps if victims have an opportunity to confront the people who have harmed them.

Hank was sentenced to camp for one year and placed on probation for three more. His parents were ordered to pay the balance of the restitution. The Judge explained to Hank that if he violated probation he would be sent to a prison for juvenile offenders. The Judge also issued a restraining order barring Hank from having contact with the Hubbard family.

Scott was charged as an adult and bail was set at $250,000. Scott's parents talked to a bail bondsman and offered their house as collateral, but its value was not high enough to cover his bail. His parents had put aside money in a savings account for Scott's college. They took out $10,000 to pay the attorney who would be representing Scott.

Ms. Perez, the attorney, told them it was going to be difficult to keep Scott out of prison.

"Scott waived his rights and spoke with the police. He implicated himself in the crime. If we were to go to trial, the prosecution would have Scott's confession. The other boys would also be called to testify against him. The jury would find Scott guilty. The question becomes, can we keep Scott out of prison? I don't think so, but I'll set up a meeting with the D.A. The biggest stumbling block for settlement of this case is the damage done by the boys. Unless Scott has a lot of money of his own, the restitution would have to come from you. Scott's portion is $44,000."

"Why is Scott being tried as an adult when he's only sixteen?" his father asked. "Hank is being tried as a juvenile."

"Hank is only fifteen," the attorney replied." In our state, a sixteen-year-old who commits a crime is automatically tried as an adult."

"You mean, if Scott had committed the crime two weeks earlier, when he was still fifteen, he would have been charged as a juvenile?"

"That's exactly right."

"But it's so unfair."

"Unfortunately, it's the law."

Ms. Perez met with the D.A. and explained her client's position. The D.A. was angry over what the boys had done and at first refused to make an offer.

"This boy is disgusting. He should rot in prison. Let's go to trial and let a jury decide."

"You and I both know the jury will find him guilty and he could go to prison for a long time. He's only sixteen and he's never been in any trouble before."

"I don't care. I think he should go to prison."

"The family might be able to pay a portion of the restitution within a month or two."

"Come and talk to me when you've got the money. Maybe I'll reconsider, but I'm not making you any promises. I don't like this boy. I'm not inclined to do him any favors."

Within a month, Scott's parents were able to put together $27,000 towards restitution. They took a second mortgage on their home and took money out of their retirement fund.

Ms. Perez returned to see the D.A. The D.A. proposed a deal where Scott would plead guilty to all three charges and go to prison for twelve months. He would be on parole for three years after his release and one-third of his pay would go to the victims until they had been fully compensated for their loss.

"I'm sure you'll explain to your client that by pleading to the Burglary charge, he'll have a strike on his record. If he ever gets in trouble again, that charge can be used to increase his sentence."

Scott refused the plea agreement.

"I'm not going to prison. Hank only got camp. Why should I have to go to prison?"

"Hank's case was heard in juvenile court. Sentencing is different in juvenile court."

"It's not fair. I want the jury to hear how unfair this case is."

"Scott, the jury isn't going to hear about Hank's sentence. It's not part of the trial. The trial is only to determine whether a defendant is guilty or not guilty. Based on the evidence, the jury will most likely find you guilty."

"I don't care. It's not fair."

Ms. Perez tried to explain to Scott that the evidence was stacked against him. She told him the jury would hear the confession he made to Detective Reynolds and that Hank would probably be called by the D.A. to testify against him. He refused to listen.

Ms. Perez spent several months preparing for trial. She interviewed the witnesses, obtained the evidence from the D.A. and organized Scott's case.

On the first day of trial, Ms. Perez and the D.A. picked the twelve jurors and two alternates who would make up Scott's jury.

On the second day, the prosecutor gave her opening statement to the jury. She explained who would testify and what they would say. Ms. Perez also gave her opening statement.

The prosecutor then called her witnesses. The police officers who arrived on the scene described in detail the extensive damage done to the house. The D.A. put up pictures of what the officers were describing. She then passed photographs to the jury members so they could see the damage close up. An agent from the insurance company testified that the total damage was $176,000. Ms. Perez cross-examined each witness.

On the third day, the Hubbards took the stand to describe the condition of the house. Then Hank, Aaron and Jared each testified about what they had done to the Hubbard's home. They described in detail Scott's participation.

On the fourth day of trial, Detective Reynolds testified about Scott's confession. Then the prosecutor announced that she had completed her case.

Ms. Perez asked for a recess. She spoke with Scott and advised him not to testify. She explained that the D.A. was free to question him and that his testimony could be more damaging than helpful. Scott decided not to testify.

"Can't my friends and family testify about me, that I'm a decent person?" Scott asked.

"This portion of the trial is to decide guilt—whether you did or didn't commit the crimes. Your character is not an issue here. If you are convicted, then your character would be important during the sentencing."

Since Scott had no alibi and there was no one to testify that he didn't commit the crime, Ms. Perez had no choice but to announce there would be no defense.

The prosecutor gave her closing argument summarizing the testimony and evidence. She asked the jury to find Scott guilty of all the charges. Ms. Perez gave her closing argument, disputing some of the prosecutor's statements and pointing out some of the discrepancies in the testimony.

The jury deliberated for four hours and returned with a guilty verdict on all three counts. The Judge set a date for Scott's sentencing.

On the day of the sentencing, the Hubbards were called to testify about the emotional pain they had suffered. After their testimony, the D.A. reviewed the evidence against Scott and asked the Judge to sentence Scott to the highest possible term in state prison.

Ms. Perez then had Scott's parents testify about Scott. She also called several of Scott's teachers and the minister from Scott's church. She asked the Judge for leniency on behalf of Scott.

"The defendant will stand. Scott Wilson, a jury has found you guilty of the crimes of Vandalism, Defacement of Property and Burglary. At your sentencing hearing today, I have listened to the testimony of your parents and friends. I have weighed their statements against the seriousness of the crimes you were found guilty of committing. I have seen the anguish your acts have caused the victims. I also took into consideration that you had been offered a plea agreement of 12 months which you refused."

"After taking all of these factors into consideration, I find the appropriate sentence to be as follows: starting with the most serious charge, Count 3, the Burglary, I sentence you to the mid-term of 3 years in state prison. On count 1, Vandalism, I sentence you to the low term of 16 months. This sentence is to run concurrent with the Burglary. On Count 2, Defacement of Property, I sentence you to the low term sentence of 16 months to run concurrent with the Burglary sentence. The defendant is committed to state prison forthwith. Officer, please escort Mr. Wilson from the courtroom. Court is adjourned."

The Law

VANDALISM
Criminal Statute Section 776.

Any person who intentionally defaces with graffiti, damages or destroys the personal property of another without their permission is guilty of vandalism.

If the damage exceeds $50,000, a violation of Criminal Statute Section 776.3 is punishable by up to one year in the county jail, or imprisonment in the state prison for 16 months, 2 years or 3 years, or by a fine of up to $20,000, or both fine and imprisonment.

DEFACEMENT OF PROPERTY
Criminal Statute Section 778

Any person who defaces property with aerosol paint with the intent to commit vandalism or graffiti, is guilty of a felony.

A violation of Criminal Statute Section 778 is punishable by up to one year in the county jail, or by imprisonment in the state prison for 16 months, 2 years or 3 years.

BURGLARY
Criminal Statute Section 324

Any person who enters a house with the intent to commit a felony (theft, rape, murder, etc.) is guilty of burglary.

A violation of Criminal Statute Section 324 is imprisonment in the state prison for 2, 3 or 5 years. In some states, a burglary of someone's home is defined as a serious crime because of the potential danger to the homeowner, and is considered a strikable offense. A strikable offense can be used to increase any future convictions.

Since the laws in each state are different, the laws cited in this book may not reflect those in your state.

Questions

1. What's the difference between "concurrent sentencing" and "consecutive sentencing"?

Concurrent sentencing means that the sentences run at the same time. As a result, Scott would remain in prison for 3 years, which is the length of his longest sentence.

Consecutive sentencing is when each sentence is served separately. In Scott's case, he would've had to serve 5 years, 8 months (3 years for the Burglary, plus 16 months for the Vandalism, plus 16 months for the Defacement of Property).

Sometimes the law allows the Judge to decide whether to run the sentences concurrently or consecutively. Other times, the law dictates how the sentences must be served and the Judge has no choice.

2. Why did Scott receive three sentences?

Trashing the Hubbard's house may have seemed like one act, but Scott broke three different laws while he was doing it. That's why he received three separate sentences.

Even if you only commit one illegal act, you might still be charged with several crimes.

3. What is the difference between a juvenile delinquency court and an adult court?

The biggest difference between juvenile courts and adult courts is in their philosophy towards people who have committed a crime. The juvenile court wants to protect the community, but it also focuses its efforts on rehabilitating kids who are caught up in criminal behavior. Adult criminal courts have one goal—to punish the offender.

Here are some of the other differences:

In most states, juveniles are not entitled to a jury trial. In adult court, a defendant is always entitled to a jury trial.

Some states try to protect the minor by not releasing his or her name to the media. In adult court, your picture could end up on the front page of the local paper.

Most juvenile delinquency proceedings are closed to the public. In adult court, the proceedings are open to the public.

In some states, a minor's juvenile delinquency record can be sealed. In adult criminal court, a person's record is open to the public.

4. Why wasn't Hank tried as an adult?

Hank was fifteen at the time he committed the crimes. In the state where Hank and Scott live, a fifteen-year-old cannot be tried as an adult. However, in other states, a fifteen-year-old like Hank could have been tried as an adult and sent to prison.

Chapter 4
Becky

Becky and Andrea were best friends. They had saved their money to go to a local amusement park. They arrived at the park early so they could spend the whole day. They ran around to as many rides as they could, and eventually stopped to have lunch.

"Should we go shopping after we eat?"

"Sure, but what kind of shopping?"

"You know! Our usual shopping."

Becky and Andrea loved to shop. They also loved to shoplift. The shoplifting had started as a dare to see who was the bravest, and had become a regular occurrence. They'd been at it for so long without being caught that they had become brazen about stealing.

After lunch, the girls wandered through the shops, trying to decide what they wanted to steal. One would ask a question of the sales person while the other would pocket an item.

There was a watch that both girls decided to lift.

"Do you think you can get two of them?" Becky asked.

"Sure. No problem."

Becky picked up a pair of earrings from a rack.

"Aren't these great?"

"They're beautiful."

"Excuse me, miss. Can you tell me how much these earrings are?"

While Becky distracted the sales person, Andrea walked over to the watches, scooped up two and proceeded to the back of the store. As she ducked around the corner, she slipped them into her pocket.

Becky thanked the sales person and continued to wander around the shop. She picked up a few small items and slipped them into her pockets.

"Let's go look at some of the other shops," Becky said.

The girls smiled and headed for the door.

"Excuse me. You're going to have to come with me."

Becky looked up to see a large man wearing a white shirt with SECURITY stenciled across it. He reached for Becky's arm. A woman in street clothes walked up and grabbed Andrea's arm.

"Security. Let's go," she said.

They started to escort the girls out of the store.

"Hey, I'm not going anywhere with you. I haven't done anything and you can't force me."

Becky pulled her arm out of the man's grasp and started to run. The security guard chased and grabbed her. During the struggle, one of her arms accidentally hit the man in the face. His nose started to gush blood. Then they lost their balance and crashed to the ground. He injured his elbow during the fall and Becky had the wind knocked out of her.

Two more security guards arrived. They yanked Becky up and handcuffed her. The girls were taken to the security building and handcuffed to a bench.

An officer came into the room to search their clothing. She confiscated the items they had stolen and left the girls in the room alone.

Andrea started to cry.

"I'm scared."

"Me too," said Becky

"Now what's going to happen?"

"I don't know."

"Maybe they'll let us go. If they don't, I'm going to be in so much trouble," Andrea said.

"Let us go? We stole a bunch of stuff. I don't think they'll just let us go."

"We could offer to pay for the stuff."

They sat together in miserable silence.

Another officer appeared. He introduced himself as the head of security.

"I've called your parents and they're on their way here. We have you on surveillance tape stealing items. We also have undercover officers who watched you steal the items and we just recorded the conversation you've been having. You're in some deep trouble, girls."

"My dad's going to kill me," Becky whimpered.

Andrea's parents arrived first, then Becky's. The security officer spoke to both families. He showed them the video tape and had them listen to the recording of the girls' conversation.

"I've notified the police. They should be here shortly," he said.

"Can we compensate you for your loss, and maybe avoid getting the police involved?" Becky's father asked.

"It's our policy to prosecute all shoplifters. And this matter goes beyond shoplifting. Becky attempted to run away and injured an officer when he tried to detain her. He had to be taken to the hospital."

When the police arrived, they spoke to the parents while the security guard filled out the complaint against Becky and Andrea.

"We're arresting your daughters and taking them to the police station for booking. Then we'll release them into your custody."

At the station, the girls were escorted into a small room. A female officer entered.

"We are going to search your body to see if you have any items hidden on you. Take off all your clothing," she ordered.

"I'm not taking off my clothes!" Andrea protested .

"It's standard procedure. You're lucky they didn't do it at the amusement park."

"I'd never let them," snapped Becky.

"You can't stop them," said the officer. "Anytime you are caught shoplifting, the store personnel have the authority to detain you and do a thorough search."

"No way!" said Andrea.

"Take your clothes off, or I will call in officers who will do it for you."

"I don't have anything hidden on me."

"Neither do I."

If you shoplift, the police have the right to thoroughly search you and your clothing.

"Then you don't have anything to worry about," the officer replied.

The girls looked at each other. Becky shrugged.

"How embarrassing."

They took off their outer clothing.

"Underwear, too."

"You must be kidding!" Andrea started to cry again.

"You don't have the right to do this!" Becky said.

"Yes we do."

The guard inspected each girl to insure no other items were hidden on her body. Then she picked up their clothes.

"Have a seat," she said pointing to a bench.

"You can't take our clothes. We're not just going to sit here naked!"

"Yes, you are. I have to search your clothes."

As the guard left the room, the girls heard the door lock behind her. An hour later, she returned with their clothes.

"You can get dressed now."

Andrea was charged with grand theft for stealing over $150 in merchandise. Becky was charged with robbery. Becky's parents took her to speak with a defense attorney.

"Being charged with robbery is very serious," the attorney explained.

"All I did was take a few things. I didn't rob anybody."

"Robbery is when you use force or fear to steal something. When you struggled with the security guard, you used force. That automatically turned the theft into a robbery."

"But it wasn't like I robbed a bank..."

"Robbery is robbery. If you were convicted of the robbery charge, it would count as a strike against you."

"What does that mean?" Her father asked.

"It means if she gets into trouble as an adult, the law requires that the sentence is doubled. It doesn't apply to this case, but it does if she gets into trouble again."

"Oh great," Becky said. "And what about this case. Do you think they'll send me to juvenile hall?"

"I'll do everything I can to keep you out of juvenile hall, but there's a possibility you might have to do time either there or in a camp."

Becky turned green.

"Your first court appearance is called an Arraignment. It's a brief appearance before a Judge. The District Attorney will read the charges against you and you'll enter a plea of not guilty. This will give me time to talk to the D.A. about a possible plea bargain."

Becky and Andrea appeared together at their arraignment. Andrea had only been charged with Grand Theft. The prosecutor made her an offer — she would plead guilty to the theft charge and receive one-hundred hours of community service. She would also be on probation for three years. No such offer was made to Becky.

"It's not fair!" Becky whined to her attorney. "Andrea only has to do community service. We stole the same things. How come they're picking on me?"

"You're not being picked on. You fought with the security guard and injured him. That changes things for you."

"But I didn't mean to hurt him. It's not like I swung at him. Besides, he was trying to stop me, and he doesn't have the right to do that. He's not a police officer."

"He does so have a right to stop you. You were a suspect in a theft. Even if you didn't hit him on purpose, in the eyes of the law it's the same as if you had intentionally punched him in the face."

A few weeks later, the attorney called Becky and her parents into his office.

"The D.A. has made an offer. You plead guilty to the robbery and receive three months in camp, three years on probation, make restitution of $300, and your parents will have to pay the medical expenses of the guard you injured. It doesn't look like the D.A. will reduce the charge, so your other option is to go to trial."

"Three months in camp! That's not fair!"

"Maybe you should have thought about that before you decided to become a thief. I will talk to the D.A. again, but before I do I want you to get me some information about yourself. I know you are in high school. If you're doing well, I want a copy of your grades."

"I had good grades this semester."

"Good. Get me a copy. Are you involved in any extra-cirricular activities?"

"Yeah. I'm on the swim team and I volunteer at the hospital one afternoon a week."

"Bring a letter from your coach and one from the hospital. Can you get me some other letters?"

"Yes. How many do you want?"

"Four or five. I want them from people who are upstanding citizens — extolling your virtues."

The next week, Becky brought her attorney everything he had asked for. He took the material to the D.A. She still refused to change her offer.

Becky's attorney called to tell her.

"The D.A. has reviewed your file, but due to the security guard's injury, she won't consider a lesser charge. If you don't take this offer, it'll be withdrawn and we'll go to trial."

"What would happen if we went to trial?"

"The prosecutor has the burden of proving you committed the crime beyond a reasonable doubt, which won't be difficult to do. She has the security guards to testify, the tape of your conversation with Andrea, the videotape of you and Andrea slipping items into your pockets, and she may even call Andrea to testify against you. She will have someone from the park testify that no one gave you permission to take the items. She'll also put on the security guard to testify that when he tried to stop you, you attacked him."

"What if I just deny everything?"

"It would be your word against the security guards' and all the other evidence. Besides, I won't represent you if you get on the stand and intentionally lie."

"What would happen if we went to trial and I lost?"

"Your sentence would probably be much more severe than the one the D.A. is offering."

Becky spoke with her parents and decided to enter a plea of guilty rather than go to trial.

On her next court date, Becky approached the front of the courtroom with her attorney. She changed her plea from not guilty to guilty.

The D.A. then addressed the Judge, "Your Honor, we have reached a plea agreement. Becky will be entering a plea of guilty to the robbery charge. In exchange for her plea agreement, she is to receive short term camp. She will begin serving that time today. She will be placed on probation for three years."

"Becky, do you understand what the D.A. has just said?" the Judge asked?

"Yes, your honor."

"You may take the plea."

The D.A. turned to Becky. "Becky, you need to listen to everything I'm saying. If you don't understand, stop me and ask your lawyer to explain. Before entering your plea today you will be giving up certain constitutional rights. Do you understand?"

"Yes," Becky said.

"You have the right to a trial. Do you understand that right and give it up?"

"Yes."

"You have the right to confront and cross examine witnesses against you. Do you understand that right and give it up?"

"Yes."

"You have the right to subpoena witnesses in your own behalf. Do you understand that right and give it up?"

"Yes."

"You have the right against self-incrimination. That means no one can make you say anything against yourself. By entering a plea today you will be incriminating yourself by admitting your guilt. Do you understand and give up that right?"

"Yes."

"Has anyone threatened you or promised you anything to get you to enter this plea today?"

"No."

"Are you entering this plea of your own free will?"

"Yes."

"The Judge could sentence you to home on probation, suitable placement in a group home or foster care, camp or prison for juvenile offenders. However, we've agreed that you will receive a short term camp commitment in exchange for your plea today. Do you understand this?"

"Yes."

"If you do well in camp and don't have any problems, you should be released in three to four months. However, the length of time you spend in camp is determined by the probation department. Do you understand this?"

"Yes."

"After your plea today, you'll be on probation for three years. You must abide by the terms and conditions of your probation. Failure to do so could result in the Judge sentencing you to additional time. Do you understand?"

"Yes."

"If you are not a citizen of the United States, your plea today could affect your legal status and you might face deportation. Do you understand?"

"Yes."

"Robbery is considered a violent offense. If you are convicted of another felony in the future as an adult, this conviction can be used to enhance any other sentence you may receive. The Judge would be required by law to sentence you to state prison and to double your sentence. If the sentence was two years, you would receive four years. Additionally, you would be required to serve at least eighty percent of the sentence before you would be eligible for release. Do you understand?"

"Yes."

"Does the court wish to inquire further?"

"No."

"Becky, to the charge of Robbery in violation of Criminal statute section 996, how do you plead?"

"Guilty."

The Judge sentenced Becky to camp. He then spoke to her.

"Becky, if somebody broke into your room and stole your television, your stereo and your clothes, what should happen to that person?"

"He should go to jail."

"Why?"

"Because he stole my stuff!"

"Didn't you steal somebody's stuff?"

Becky shrugged. "It's different. The stuff I took didn't really belong to anybody."

"It belongs to the amusement park."

"Yeah, but that's not a real person."

"You mean it's okay to steal from a company but not a person?"

"Ah..."

"Becky, are you mad at yourself because you stole or are you mad because you got caught?"

Becky thought for a moment. "Both."

"You should be disappointed in yourself. I hope you'll use your time in camp to think about what you did, and take some action to assure it will never happen again."

The Judge turned towards the bailiff.

"Please remand her into custody."

The Law

THEFT
Criminal Statute Section 1400

Every person who takes or steals the personal property of another is guilty of theft.

PETTY THEFT
Criminal Statute Section 1401

When the money or personal property taken is of a value below $100, the crime is petty theft, a misdemeanor.

GRAND THEFT
Criminal Statute Section 1402

When the money or personal property taken is of a value exceeding $100, the crime is grand theft, a felony.

ROBBERY
Criminal Statute Section 996

Robbery is the taking of personal property of another, from his person or immediate presence, against his will accomplished by force or fear. Robbery is a felony punishable by 4, 5 or 6 years in prison.

Since the laws in each state are different, the laws cited in this book may not reflect those in your state.

Questions

1. Why was Becky charged with Robbery instead of Theft?

Once Becky used force, it changed the crime from a theft to a robbery. It doesn't matter if the force was used while the item was being stolen or while she was being apprehended. As long as she was in possession of stolen property and used force while trying to escape, the crime went from theft to robbery.

Robbery is considered a violent crime and is a much more serious offense than a theft.

2. Is being charged with robbery in a juvenile court different than being charged with robbery in an adult court?

The crime of robbery is a felony whether you are charged in adult court or juvenile court. However, there are different sentencing options available for juveniles. A juvenile who is tried in juvenile court cannot be sentenced to county jail or state prison. Those are sentences only given in adult court.

3. Could Becky have been charged as an adult and be sent to prison?

Yes, but it would depend on Becky's age and the state where she lived. In some states, any minor under eighteen who is charged with a violation of a criminal statute is automatically sent to juvenile court. The prosecutor then reviews the facts of the crime and the minor's prior criminal history to determine if the minor should be sent to adult court.

If Becky's case had been sent to adult court and she had been convicted, it is possible she could have received a prison sentence. However, it's more likely she would have received a lesser sentence, which may have included time in county jail.

4. *What is the "strike law"?*

More than thirty states have passed a strike law. A strike law means a person who has been convicted of a crime that is considered serious or violent can receive a much longer sentence for future crimes he or she commits. In some states, an adult with two prior strikes who is convicted of a 3rd felony is automatically sent to prison for 25 years to life.

Chapter 5

Justin & Brad

Justin and Brad had been best friends since they were in fifth grade. They were closer than most brothers and did almost everything together. They were well-liked at school and both had been on their high school football team. Most nights they worked out with their friends in a garage that Justin's parents had let them convert into a gym.

Justin worked as an assistant manager for a pizza restaurant. He lived at home with his parents and younger sister. Brad worked at his family's business. He lived with his mom and older brother.

After completing high school, Justin and Brad went to the local community college. They both hoped to become police officers.

It was the middle of summer and Justin was about to celebrate his nineteenth birthday. He and Brad had planned a trip to the beach. The weather was sunny and warm. Brad drove and Justin navigated from the passenger's seat. Music blasted on the radio as Brad pulled onto the freeway and started towards the beach.

The speed limit was 65 miles per hour, but they lived in a rural area and the freeway wasn't very crowded. Brad was an excellent driver who almost always used good judgment. He was doing about 75 miles per hour.

About ten minutes into the trip, Brad pulled into the slower lane while still doing 75. His attention was distracted for a moment. When he turned his eyes back to the road, the car had drifted onto the shoulder. Brad over-corrected, swinging the steering wheel to the left. The car hit some gravel, careened out of control and flipped over three times.

A car traveling behind the boys came on the scene and stopped. The driver, Henry Castle, grabbed his car phone and called 911. Then he ran to the car to help. He went to the driver's side and knelt down. The door had been torn away, but the car was so badly crushed he couldn't reach Brad. He was frightened by the amount of blood that was pooling on the road.

Henry ran to the other side of the car to see if he could pull Brad out, but the car was upside down and the roof had been smashed in. He couldn't get the door open. As he ran back to the driver's side, he noticed a torn pantsleg laying on the road. When he looked down he realized that it held part of a leg.

Just then a police cruiser arrived. The officer immediately called for additional help. Within minutes the paramedics and a fire engine arrived. They tried to reach Brad using the jaws of life. One of the para-medics picked up the leg and packed it in ice.

After about thirty minutes, the firemen were able to reach Brad. He was unconscious from the loss of blood where his leg had been torn off during the accident. The paramedics were finally able to put a tourniquet around the leg. They were still unable to free Brad because his arm was trapped in the crushed wreckage. They tried for the next half hour to get him out, but with no luck.

Brad was an excellent driver who almost always used good judgment.

A doctor from the hospital arrived. He assessed Brad's condition and feared that he would die within minutes if he wasn't removed from the car. To save Brad's life, he amputated the arm below the elbow. A helicopter was waiting, and Brad was transported to the trauma center.

It was only after they removed Brad that the paramedics realized there was another person trapped in the car. They pulled Justin from the car and declared him dead at the scene.

Brad's condition was touch and go for several days. During the accident, Brad's door had been flung open and his leg had been caught between the car and the pavement. The doctors tried to reattach his leg, but the damage had been too severe.

Brad was still unconscious when Justin was buried. Brad's parents attended the funeral; they stood and watched as Justin's mom and dad buried their 19-year-old son, wondering if they would have to do the same for Brad.

Brad didn't die, but his recovery was slow and painful.

The police began an investigation immediately after the accident. They had an accident reconstructionist measure the roadway and the skidmarks. He examined Brad's vehicle and wrote a report that stated the cause of the accident was excessive speed. He estimated that Brad had been driving about 75 miles an hour, which was ten miles over the speed limit. He concluded that if

Brad had not been speeding, he would not have lost control of the car and Justin would have survived.

After receiving the report, the detective assigned to the case came to the hospital to interview Brad. Brad told the detective what he could remember. He admitted that he had been going over 65.

The detective concluded that Brad was negligent in speeding, and that his negligent behavior was the cause of Justin's death. He submitted his report to the district attorney's office and recommended that the prosecutor file charges against Brad.

Within a month, Brad had recovered sufficiently to be released from the hospital. He needed to be in a wheelchair until his leg and arm had healed enough to be fit for prosthetic devices.

After his release, Brad met with a defense attorney who his parents had hired to represent him. She explained the criminal statute that Brad was being charged with — felony Vehicular Manslaughter. The D.A. had made an offer of 2 years in prison. If Brad decided against the offer, he would face a trial.

Several days later, Brad appeared at court. Brad's attorney asked for a chamber's conference with the Judge and the D.A. She would try to convince the D.A. to reduce the charge against Brad.

Back in his chambers, the Judge said, "This is a difficult case. One boy is dead and the other is badly maimed. What's your position on this, Mr. Dillon?" he asked the D.A.

"I've spoken with the deceased boy's mother. She is not interested in seeing Brad go to jail. Now that I have a more complete picture of the case, I'd be willing to let Brad plead to a misdemeanor Vehicular Manslaughter. I would waive the jail time and ask for community service."

"I'd have to talk to my client, but I think he would be agreeable. The only problem would be the community service. With his injuries, I don't think there is much he can do in the way of community service."

"Community service is quite capable of dealing with people who have handicaps. They'll find something for him. Go talk to your client," the Judge said.

The Law

Vehicular Manslaughter
Criminal Statute Section 487.

Vehicular Manslaughter is:

(a) operating a vehicle in the commission of an unlawful act, but without gross negligence, which might produce death;

(b) operating a vehicle in the commission of an unlawful act, with gross negligence, which might produce death.

A violation of Criminal Code Section 487 is punishable as follows: (a) imprisonment in the county jail for one year; (b) imprisonment in the state prison for two, four or six years.

Brad was charged with felony Manslaughter which was later reduced to misdemeanor manslaughter. To be guilty of Manslaughter the following elements must be proven:

1. The suspect must be operating a motor vehicle;

2. The suspect must be committing an unlawful act which might produce death.

Since the laws in each state are different, the laws cited in this book may not reflect those in your state.

Questions

1. What's the difference between a felony and a misdemeanor?

A felony is a more serious crime than a misdemeanor. If you are convicted of a felony, you could be sent to state prison for many years depending upon the crime and your past criminal history.

A misdemeanor is a less serious offense. If you are convicted of a misdemeanor, your sentence can be anywhere from 0 to 365 days in the county jail.

2. Who decided to charge Brad with a felony?

The decision to charge as a felony or misdemeanor is made by the District Attorney's office. The District Attorney's office is in charge of prosecuting people who have been accused of crimes. An attorney at the D.A.'s office reviews the facts in the police reports and determines if a case should be filed as a felony or a misdemeanor.

In this case, the D.A. decided to reduce the charge from a felony to a misdemeanor. This allowed him to offer Brad community service instead of time in prison, which the felony charge would have required.

3. Why was Brad charged with felony Manslaughter instead of misdemeanor Manslaughter?

There are two types of Manslaughter: felony Manslaughter and misdemeanor Manslaughter. The difference between the two is the degree of negligence. To be charged with felony manslaughter, there must be evidence of gross negligence. Negligence means you failed to take reasonable care. Gross negligence means you showed a reckless disregard for another's life.

While the D.A. in Brad's case originally charged him with a felony, another D.A. might have viewed the facts differently and filed the case as a misdemeanor. A third D.A. might have refused to make an offer and forced Brad to go to trial.

Not all states have both felony and misdemeanor manslaughter. In some states, the D.A. might have no choice but to file the case as a felony.

4. Why was Brad charged with Justin's death when he really wasn't driving that fast?

First of all, speeding is speeding even if it is only one mile over the speed limit. Second, Brad admitted to speeding which is an unlawful act. Third, the reconstructionist's report stated that Brad's excessive speed had caused Justin's death. That is sufficient evidence to charge Brad with Manslaughter.

Statistics

Motor vehicle fatalities are the number one killer of teenagers and other young adults.

Chapter 6
Cheryl

Cheryl had always been a straight 'A' student. Her SAT scores were high enough to get her into any college, including her dream school, Harvard.

The one course Cheryl had been struggling with was chemistry, but she thought she'd done well on her final exam. When she got her report card, she was mortified to see her grade — 'C'. Cheryl felt her chances of being accepted into Harvard were slipping away.

"What am I going to do?" she asked herself. She worried about her grades all night.

The next day, she went to visit her friend, Tracy.

"I'll never get into Harvard now," Cheryl wailed. "It's what I wanted more than anything!"

"What if the grade could be changed?" Tracy asked.

"I already talked to the teacher. She said I got a better grade than I deserved."

"No, I mean what if someone could change the grade?"

"I don't understand what you're saying."

"Come on. I'll show you."

They walked down the street to another house. Tracy knocked on the door.

"Rick!" she called.

A disheveled young man came to the door. The hair on the top of his head was sticking straight up and he was wearing his pajamas at two in the afternoon.

"He's sick. We should go," Cheryl whispered.

"He's not sick. This is his usual attire. Can we come in?"

"Sure."

They followed Rick upstairs to his bedroom. It was filled with electronic equipment.

"Rick's a computer genius. He's studying computer science at State University," Tracy said.

"Hey Rick, Cheryl's got a problem. She wants to go to Harvard, but kind of screwed up this semester. She just got a 'C' in chemistry. Can you help her?"

"What kind of help?"

"You know, change the grade. Everyone knows you're the best when it comes to hacking," Tracy said.

"What's in it for me?" Rick asked.

"You mean you could really change my grade?"

"For a price," Rick said.

"How much do you want?"

"Two hundred bucks."

"I'll have to go to the bank and get money out of my savings account. I can't get it until Monday," Cheryl said.

"Whatever."

"Thanks, Rick. We'll see you Monday after school," Tracy said. She leaned over and kissed him on the cheek.

Cheryl brought the money on Monday. Rick asked her for her full name, birth date and the name of her school.

"How long will this take?" Cheryl asked.

"Call me in a few days."

Cheryl went home and tried not to think about Harvard and her grades.

The next day Cheryl saw Tracy.

"So?" Tracy asked.

"I'm supposed to call him in a few days," Cheryl whispered to Tracy.

"A few days? Let's call him now!"

They went to a pay phone.

"Rick, Tracy. How's it going?" Tracy listened. "Okay. Okay. Yeah. Bye."

Tracy hung up the phone.

"Guess you better get ready for that cold weather on the east coast."

"What?" Cheryl yelled.

"It's done."

"You're kidding!" Cheryl said, grabbing Tracy, "What did he say?"

"He said it's done."

"This is great. I can't believe it. Just in time to have my grades sent to Harvard."

Time passed. Finally the letter arrived admitting Cheryl to Harvard. She was walking on air. Her parents took her out to celebrate. She then called her friend Tracy, who called her friend Denise to tell her the news.

Denise was dumbfounded.

"I was in Chemistry with her. She got a 'C'. How did she get into Harvard?"

Not being one to keep a secret, Tracy told Denise how she had helped Cheryl get her grade changed.

Denise was upset. When she hung up the phone, she couldn't stop pacing back and forth. What Cheryl and Tracy had done was wrong. The more she thought about it, the more enraged she became.

After a sleepless night, Denise wrote a note to the chemistry teacher, but she didn't sign it.

Dear Mr. Milgard,

> I have been told that Cheryl Michaelson hired a computer hacker to change her Chemistry grade from a C to an A. Tracy Lowry helped her. Could you check it out?

Denise went to the school office. While everyone was busy, she slipped the note into Mr. Milgard's message box. She quickly walked away, hoping no one had noticed her.

One week later, Cheryl was sitting in class, watching the clock, when a student came in with a note for the teacher.

"Cheryl, could you go to the Principal's office, please."

Cheryl wasn't concerned. She figured Mr. Rainier wanted to congratulate her for getting into Harvard. She walked up to the Principal's secretary.

"Hi, Mrs. Grant. Mr. Rainier wants to see me."

Mrs. Grant motioned towards the door. Cheryl was surprised to see her parents in Mr. Rainier's office.

"Cheryl, I asked your parents to be here while I talk to you. It's come to our attention that you may have paid someone to break into our school computer to change your chemistry grade."

Mr. Rainier glanced down at some papers.

"I have a copy of your teacher's grade report. It indicates a 'C' in Chemistry. I also have a printout from the school's computer. It indicates an 'A' in Chemistry. Do you know anything about this?"

"Ah, no. Absolutely not. I don't know why there's a difference. Maybe somebody made a mistake when they were putting in the grades."

"Cheryl, we know someone has tampered with our computer program. If you know anything about this, this is your chance to come clean," Mr. Rainier advised.

Cheryl glanced at her parents.

"I don't know anything!"

Mr. Rainier left the office for a moment. When he returned a woman was with him.

"Cheryl, this is Officer Vaughn. She's investigating the break-in to our computer."

"I've just come from speaking with Richard Hawks. He told us that he was contacted by Tracy Lowry and her friend, Cheryl Michaelson. They asked him to break into the computer and change Cheryl's grade in Chemistry.

Mr. Rainier says you didn't know anything about this, Cheryl. Is that the truth?"

Cheryl started to shiver.

"I don't know anybody named Richard."

"You were probably introduced to him as 'Rick'."

Cheryl shook her head.

"Don't know him."

"Cheryl, I'm going to read you your rights."

After Officer Vaughn read Cheryl her Constitutional rights, she asked if Cheryl would waive her rights and consent to an interview.

"I'll be glad to talk to you, but I don't know anything," Cheryl said.

"Cheryl, why do you think Rick says he knows you?"

"I don't know. I told you, I don't know anyone named Rick."

Officer Vaughn stood up.

"I'll be right back. My partner's talking to Tracy. I want to see how it's going."

Cheryl felt numb. How was she going to explain this?

Her father's voice broke the silence.

"Cheryl, if you were somehow involved in this, you need to tell the officer. We know you wouldn't intentionally do anything wrong, but you might know something that can help the officer with the investigation."

"We have a real problem here, Cheryl."

The officer reentered the room. She sat down and sighed.

"We have a real problem here, Cheryl. Tracy says she took you to Rick's house and introduced you to him, and that you made arrangements to have Rick alter your grade. Tracy also said that you took two hundred dollars out of your savings account and paid it to Rick."

"Okay. Maybe Tracy did introduce me to Rick, and we talked about my grades, but I didn't tell him to change the grades. He just did it on his own."

"What about the money?"

"I took out some money but it was to buy some clothes."

"So then you'll have the receipts because Rick said you paid him two hundred dollars," Officer Vaughn said.

"He's the one who did everything. I didn't do anything. I just wanted to go to Harvard!"

"Cheryl! How could you?" Her mother said in shock.

"You hired someone to change your grades so you could get into Harvard? Is that what you're saying?" her father yelled.

"I'm sorry," the officer interrupted. "I have to take Cheryl to the police station."

"But I didn't do anything. He did it! I had to get into Harvard. Do you think they would have accepted me with a 'C'? Well, they wouldn't. So I talked to Rick, but I didn't have anything to do with breaking into the computer."

"It doesn't matter that you didn't change the grade yourself. By hiring someone to commit a crime, you're as guilty as the person who actually committed the act," the officer explained.

Cheryl was taken to the police station. Since she was seventeen, she was charged as a minor with Conspiracy to commit Computer Fraud. She was released to her parent's custody. Her first court date was in two weeks.

She was expelled from high school and had to enroll in an alternative school. The police notified Harvard of the investigation, and Cheryl received a letter saying that her acceptance was suspended pending the outcome of the case.

When Cheryl went to court, Tracy was also there. Her attorney explained to her that Tracy had been charged on the same complaint.

"Where's Rick?" Cheryl asked.

"He'll be charged as an adult," her attorney explained. "Today we're here for the Arraignment. The charges will be read and you'll enter a plea of not guilty."

When the case was called, Cheryl and Tracy stood in front of the Judge with their attorneys and entered their not guilty pleas. The next court date was set.

"Now what happens?" Cheryl asked her attorney?

"As I told you when we first met, it's up to you. If you want me to negotiate with the District Attorney, I will try, or you can go to trial."

"Can we win if I go to trial?"

"Stranger things have happened, but it's pretty unlikely. They have your statement that you made to Detective Vaughn. They have Tracy's statement admitting that you and she were involved. Rick also implicated you. They have the changes to your school records, and the bank records showing that you withdrew the $200. If you were a juror and heard this evidence, how would you decide?"

"This is so depressing. Go ahead and talk to the D.A. Do you think I'll have to go to jail?"

"Maybe."

Tracy called Cheryl when she got home.

"I don't understand why I'm being charged," Tracy said. "I didn't do anything. I introduced you, but Rick was the one who changed the grade."

"My attorney said that we're charged with conspiracy because we knew Rick was committing a crime and he did it because we asked him to. I have to hang up now. I'm grounded and I'm not supposed to be talking on the phone."

"Do you think we will get in a lot of trouble?"

"I will," Cheryl said, choking back tears. "I gotta go."

A few weeks later, Cheryl received a call from her attorney.

"Rick has entered into a plea agreement. He pled to the computer fraud charge and will receive community service in exchange for testifying against you and Tracy. The D.A. on your case has offered you a deal. He's agreed to reduce the charge to a misdemeanor. He wanted you to do ninety days in Juvenile Hall, but I convinced him to give you ninety days of electronic monitoring instead. They'll put a bracelet around your ankle and you'll be confined to your home. If you leave without permission, your probation will be violated and the Judge could put you in Juvenile Hall. You'll also be on probation for three years, and a fine of one-thousand dollars will be imposed."

"Is it a good deal?"

"It's a great deal. You won't have a felony on your record, which is good."

"Okay. I'll take the deal."

The Laws

COMPUTER FRAUD
Criminal Statute Section 17354

Any person who knowingly and without permission accesses any computer or computer program, or makes any alteration or deletion of information in a computer system is guilty of the crime of computer fraud.

A violation of Criminal Code Section 17354 is punishable by imprisonment in the state prison from 16 months up to 3 years, and a fine of up to $5,000, or by imprisonment in the county jail for up to 1 year and a fine of up to$2,500.

Any property of the defendant used in committing a violation of Criminal Code section 17354 is subject to forfeiture.

CRIMINAL CONSPIRACY
Criminal Statute Section 171

If two or more people conspire to commit any crime they have committed a criminal conspiracy.

The punishment for violation of Criminal Statute 171 will be determined by the underlying criminal charge.

Since the laws in each state are different, the laws cited in this book may not reflect those in your state.

Questions

1. Cheryl didn't break into the computer, so why is she guilty?

You do not have to be the person who commits the crime to be guilty of the crime. Cheryl and Tracy are just as guilty as Rick because they entered into an agreement with him knowing that what they had asked him to do was illegal.

2. What is a plea bargain?

This is when the District Attorney makes an offer to resolve the case before it goes to trial. The offer is made to the defendant and his or her attorney. It requires the defendant to enter a plea of guilty to one or more of the charges in return for a sentence that is agreed upon ahead of time.

If Cheryl had gone to trial and been found guilty, the Judge could have sentenced her to juvenile hall or boot camp. By entering into the plea agreement, Cheryl admitted her guilt and received a lighter sentence.

3. Cheryl was seventeen, but was still charged as a minor. Scott, from Chapter 3, was sixteen, but he was charged as an adult. How come?

The laws regarding age vary from state to state. It also depends on the type of crime that's been committed.

4. What is electronic monitoring?

An electronic bracelet is attached to your ankle. An electronic device in the bracelet monitors where you are at all times. If you leave the house without authorization or attempt to take the bracelet off, the electronic device alerts the authorities.

Attempting to remove the electronic bracelet or leaving the house without authorization can be a probation violation.

5. If you were Denise, would you have turned Cheryl in? When do you have a responsibility to report crime? What if you were the kid who didn't get into college because Cheryl cheated and took your place?

Chapter 7
Jenny

Jenny's family immigrated to the United States when she was two-years-old. Her parents had four more children after coming here. She was the oldest and her mother expected her to help with the younger children. Jenny enjoyed school and was a good student, but finding the time and a quiet place to study was difficult.

Jenny's father worked as a cook in a restaurant, and on Sundays the whole family would go to the restaurant to eat dinner. Her parents were good people who loved their children and spent as much time with them as possible.

When Jenny started junior high, she became more and more embarrassed by her parents. They worked hard, but were poor and didn't speak English very well. Jenny was particularly ashamed of their accents. She wished they were more like the families she saw on television. She was also self-conscious about her clothes, and dreamed of having the designer clothes that some of the other girls at school wore. Most of her clothes were made by her mother or were purchased secondhand.

When Jenny was in eighth grade, her father suddenly died of a stroke. He'd always seemed so strong, and then one day he was gone. She didn't even get to say goodbye.

Jenny's parents had always struggled with money, but now the family was barely able to manage. Jenny's mother took a second full-time job. She would leave at 7:00 a.m. to get to her first job as a seamstress. At her second job, she worked on a cleaning crew in an office building. She finished at 2:00 a.m., came home, slept for four hours and started her day again. She worked all day Saturday at the sewing shop for extra money. Sunday was her one day off, and she was too exhausted to do more than sleep.

With her mother working so much, the care of the smaller children fell to Jenny. Jenny's days now started at 6:00 a.m. She would wake up her brothers and sisters and get them ready for school. She also made their breakfast and lunch. After school, she had to come home right away because her youngest brother was only four and couldn't stay by himself. As soon as she came home, Jenny started dinner. After she got everyone fed and bathed, she would try to find time to do her homework. Her grades were slipping and her teachers were concerned.

Jenny's English teacher sent a note home asking her mother to come in for a conference. Jenny translated the note for her mom, who said she couldn't come in because of her work schedule. Jenny was called into the Principal's office. He listened to her story, and agreed to forego the meeting if Jenny improved her grades. She left with a heavy feeling. She couldn't figure out where she would get more time to study.

She started going to bed later and getting up earlier. Her grades improved enough to keep her from drawing attention to herself, but she began to get sick a lot. Somehow, she made it through the eighth grade and into high school. That's when she met Andre.

Jenny thought Andre was a student because he was usually at school. Then she discovered he had dropped out. He told her he lived in the neighborhood. He often walked her home at the end of the day, and sometimes would stay for dinner.

Jenny knew her mother wouldn't approve of Andre. He was eighteen, a gang member, and had tattoos. Andre began asking Jenny to come out with him at night. She refused because she couldn't leave her brothers and sisters alone.

One night she finally gave in. She put the kids to bed and followed Andre to a park where the other gang members hung out. Everyone came up to Andre and talked to him. Jenny was impressed. One of the girls told her that Andre was the second in command. The others listened to him and followed his lead. The night was fun with everyone talking and listening to music. Some of the guys were drinking, but not Andre. Jenny liked the feeling of friendship.

The next day, Andre came by with three bags of groceries. Jenny was shocked by the amount of food. She told him she couldn't accept it. He laughed and set the bags down in the kitchen. Then he left. Jenny wondered how she was going to explain all of the candy, ice cream and sodas to her mom. Fortunately, her mom was too tired to notice.

Jenny didn't see Andre for several days and worried that he had forgotten her. She saw one of the girls from the park and asked her about Andre. She smiled and told Jenny not to worry, that he'd be back soon.

About a week later, Jenny took her brothers and sisters to the local park for a picnic. As they were leaving, she saw Andre lounging under a tree. He walked home with her and gave her a small box. Jenny opened it and found a beautiful gold necklace.

That night they went to the park. Once again, Jenny saw how much the others admired Andre. Some of the guys came up to Andre and asked about the "trip." Andre told them the trip was fine. His answer made it clear that he didn't want to talk about it. Jenny enjoyed talking to the other girls. They all admired the necklace that Andre had given her.

"You're Andre's girl now."

Each afternoon, Andre would meet Jenny after school and walk home with her. Then he would leave, saying he had to go back to work. When she asked him what he did, he said he was a salesman. When she asked where he worked, he said he was self-employed. Jenny suspected he was involved with something illegal, but she tried not to think about it.

One day as Jenny and Andre walked home, Andre asked if she would keep some money for him. She agreed. Andre came to the house after the kids were in bed and gave her a brown paper bag. He asked Jenny to hide it where it would be safe. He explained that it was money from his business and that he didn't want to put it in the bank. Jenny moved the dresser in her room and hid the money behind it. She felt good about helping Andre after everything he had done for her.

Several weeks later, Andre asked for the money. Jenny retrieved it from the hiding place and gave it to him. Andre took the money out of the bag and counted it. Jenny was shocked. She'd never seen so much money in her entire life. Andre gave her $50.00, kissed her and left.

$50.00! No one had ever given Jenny that much money. She didn't know what to do with it! She bought her mother a new skirt and new clothes for brothers and sisters. She told her mom that she had made extra money babysitting some of the neighborhood kids.

Andre continued to ask Jenny to hide packages for him. She was glad to do it. Each time he would give her some money, which Andre said was her storage fee. She never looked inside the packages, she only hid them.

One night several months later, Jenny was awakened by a knock on the door. She opened it to six police officers — some in uniform, some in street clothes. One of the officers introduced himself as Detective Diehl. He asked if they could search the house. Jenny was afraid, but said okay.

The police woke the younger children and brought them into the living room. They sat huddled on the couch with Jenny as the police took out all the items from the cupboards and closets. One of the officers brought in a dog. Detective Diehl explained that the dog was specially trained to sniff out drugs. When the dog walked into the room where Jenny slept, he started barking and clawing at the dresser. The police moved the dresser and pulled the bag from its hiding place.

Detective Diehl asked Jenny if he could look inside the bag. Jenny said it wasn't hers, but that she thought it would be okay. He opened it and emptied the contents onto the table. Jenny saw a roll of money the size of a soda can with a $100 bill on the outside. She also saw at least fifty small white packages.

"What are those?" she asked the detective. He took one of the packages and opened it up. It contained white powder. Another officer placed a small amount of the powder in a test tube with some clear liquid. As soon as the powder touched the liquid it turned purple.

"It's Meth."

Detective Diehl asked Jenny if she knew that the bag contained illegal drugs. She said no, that she was only holding it for her friend, Andre. The detective counted more than fifty small packets and over $5,000 dollars in cash. He then read Jenny her rights, and asked her if she would speak with him. She agreed.

"Jenny, what do you know about Andre? Did you know he was a member of a gang?"

"Yes. I knew, but that doesn't make him a bad person."

"Did you know he was selling drugs?"

"No."

"What did you think was in the bag?"

"I thought there was money in it."

"Where do you think Andre would get this kind of money?"

"I didn't know how much money was in there."

"How many times have you held these bags for Andre?"

"I don't know. Maybe five or six times in the last couple of months."

"Where'd you think he was getting all this money?"

"Working."

"Did he ever tell you he had a job? Did you ever see him go to work? Did you ever see his paycheck? Of course not, you knew he was selling drugs and that's where he got his money. You knew that, didn't you?"

Jenny looked down at her feet.

"I guess I sort of knew."

The Detective shook his head and walked away.

Jenny's mother arrived home, and the detective explained to her what they had found. She started to cry, saying that Jenny was a good girl. Detective Diehl said that he was going to arrest Jenny and take her to the juvenile detention facility. He had Jenny put her hands behind her back and then he handcuffed her.

The next morning, Detective Diehl went to the District Attorney's office and gave his police report to the attorney in charge of filing petitions against

When the police dog walked into the room where Jenny slept,
he started barking and clawing at the dresser.

juveniles. The D.A. then filed a delinquency petition against Jenny for Possession for Sale of Drugs and Providing Storage for Drugs.

Jenny was brought into juvenile court before a Judge. The Judge was angry because of the large quantity of drugs found. A hearing was held to determine if Jenny should be released from custody pending her trial. The Judge didn't want to release her into her mother's custody because he said there wasn't enough supervision at home. He declared Jenny a ward of the court. Her mother asked if Jenny could be released on bail. The Judge explained that minors were not entitled to bail. They were either released into the custody of a parent or they remained in custody of the court.

Several days later, Jenny's court-appointed attorney told her that Detective Diehl wanted to speak with her. She cried when she saw the detective, and asked when she could go home. He told her it might be a long time. He asked her about Andre again, but Jenny didn't know much. She didn't know where he lived and she didn't know his last name. She knew that Andre hung out at the park and she gave the Detective Andre's pager number. He asked her where Andre got the drugs. Jenny told him she didn't know.

"I told you, I didn't know there were drugs in the bag."

She wanted Detective Diehl to understand that she was only holding the bag for Andre and that it wasn't hers, but she could tell he didn't believe her. Even her own attorney didn't believe her. Everyone thought she knew about the drugs and was involved in selling them. Her own mother was skeptical about Jenny's honesty.

"You're a smart girl," she said. "Maybe you didn't look in the bag, but you knew what was going on."

When Jenny had been in custody about a month, her attorney arrived and said the D.A. had offered a deal. If she pled guilty to Providing a Room for Storage of a Controlled Substance as a felony, the D.A. would drop the Possession for Sale charge. Jenny would go to camp for six months and then be released. After her release, she would be on probation for two years. She couldn't get into any trouble during her probation or the Judge would put her in prison for youthful offenders.

Her attorney also explained that Jenny had been charged with a felony which was much more serious than a misdemeanor. If she didn't take the deal she would go to trial. He explained that in a juvenile trial, there wasn't a jury — only a Judge who decided the case. The detective would testify that he found the drugs in her house along with all the money, and that Andre had never been found by the police. She could testify in her own behalf, but they didn't have any witnesses to back up her story. With the money and large quantity of drugs found in her house, she would probably be convicted and the Judge might sentence her to prison for youthful offenders.

Jenny felt that she had no alternative but to take the deal. When she went to court the next day, she plead guilty to the charge against her and was sentenced to boot camp for six months.

At camp, Jenny didn't have the responsibility of caring for her mother, brothers and sisters, but she did miss her family. Her mother wrote to her, but the camp was too far away for her to visit.

Jenny lived in a dormitory with twelve other girls. The cots were in one big room. Everyone had to get up at 6:30. Jenny had to get cleaned-up and dressed in fifteen minutes. The bathroom was small and all twelve girls would crowd in. There were two toilets and two sinks, all out in the open. There was no privacy. Breakfast was over at 7:15. If you didn't get there in time, you didn't eat. After breakfast, each girl would be assigned a job. It was always manual labor and could be anything from cleaning the toilets or emptying the garbage to washing dishes or pulling weeds. At 9:00 a.m., classes started. Everyone attended school at camp — no excuses.

They broke for lunch at noon. Classes started again at 12:30 and would finish at 3:30. Everyone was assigned to work from 3:30 to 5:00. At 5:00 p.m., dinner was served. From 5:30 to 8:00, they did homework. From 8:00 to 9:00, the girls had free time to take a shower, write letters or talk with the other girls. Lights were out at 9:00 p.m. Sunday was the only day they didn't have to go to school. There were church services in the morning, and everyone worked the rest of the day at their assigned tasks.

All the girls participated in counseling classes. The counselor made them talk about their crimes and what had led them into trouble. The counselor always expressed the importance of each person taking responsibility for her behavior. Jenny thought about that a lot.

At first, she had blamed Andre for her trouble. After awhile, she started to realize that she was the one to blame. She knew Andre was a gang member, that he didn't have a regular job, and that the bags he had her hide probably contained money and drugs. She began to realize that no one gets something for nothing. If it seems too good to be true, it probably is.

Jenny worked hard in school and did well. She started to think about the future, and maybe going to college after high school.

Before her release from camp, Jenny was visited by her Probation Officer. Her P.O. said that she had to stay out of trouble and that she couldn't associate with Andre or anyone else in the gang. Jenny agreed, knowing full well she would never associate with them again. Her P.O. told her she had to go back to school and stay in school. She also arranged for Jenny and her mother to attend family counseling together.

After six months, Jenny was released from camp. She returned home and went back to school. She's in college now and would have liked to become a probation officer, but her criminal record makes her ineligible for that type of career.

The Law

POSSESSION FOR SALE OF A CONTROLLED SUBSTANCE
Criminal Statute Section 509

Any person who sells, manages, administers, gives away or offers to sell any controlled substance which is a narcotic drug has committed an unlawful act.

A violation of Criminal Code Section 509 is punishable by imprisonment in the state prison for 3, 4, or 5 years.

PROVIDING A ROOM FOR STORAGE AND/OR
DISTRIBUTION OF A CONTROLLED SUBSTANCE
Criminal Statute Section 515

Any person who has under his or her management or control any building, room, space, or enclosure, who knowingly makes available with or without compensation, for the purpose of storing or distributing a controlled substance, has committed an unlawful act.

A violation of Criminal Code Section 515 is punishable by imprisonment in the county jail for not more than 1 year or in state prison for 16 months, 2 years or 3 years.

Since the laws in each state are different, the laws cited in this book may not reflect those in your state.

Questions

1. Why was Jenny charged with selling drugs when she didn't sell any drugs?

You don't have to be caught selling to be charged with selling. Jenny had in her possession a large quantity of drugs wrapped in individual packets, plus a large sum of money. From those facts, the police and courts are going to assume she was selling drugs.

Also, while she wasn't actually selling the drugs herself, she participated in selling by hiding drugs that were then sold by Andre.

If only a small amount of drugs had been found in the bag and there had been no money, the police would have assumed that the drugs were for personal use. Jenny would have been charged with possession of a controlled substance and not sales.

2. Jenny says she didn't know that the package from Andre contained drugs. If this were true, would she be innocent?

No. Jenny knew that Andre was a gang member. She agreed to keep mysterious packages for him, and she suspected he was involved with drugs. A reasonable person should have suspected the bags contained drugs.

Even if you don't have an active role, any kind of involvement with criminal activity is dangerous. The police are going to assume you are fully involved and charge you accordingly.

3. What is bail?

Bail is the amount of money a defendant must pay to be released from custody while awaiting his or her trial. The amount of bail is determined by the crime the defendant has been accused of and the defendant's prior criminal history. The money is to guarantee that the defendant will return for his or her court dates. If a defendant fails to appear in court, the money will be forfeited.

If a defendant cannot post bail, he or she will remain in custody until the outcome of the case is decided.

4. Why wasn't Jenny released on bail?

A minor who is charged with a crime in juvenile court is not entitled to bail. The Judge will either release the minor to the custody of a parent or guardian, or the minor will remain at a juvenile detention center pending the outcome of the case.

5. How does the Judge decide to keep or release a minor?

If the judge thinks the minor is a threat to the people in the community, or has inadequate supervision at home, the minor will remain in custody.

Chapter 8
Jimmy

Jimmy never fit in. He didn't like sports and he didn't do well in school. By the time he was thirteen, he wore all black and used makeup to whiten his face. His mom and dad hated the way he dressed and the kids at school made fun of him, but at least they were staring to notice. It was better than getting no attention at all.

Jimmy made friends with some of the kids who were into the Gothic lifestyle. His friends were not exactly mainstream. They talked about the power of the sky and the earth, and cast spells on people who upset them. They also drank and used a lot of drugs.

Jimmy and his friends often hung out at the mall. Eventually, they started shoplifting.

One time, the owner of a store caught Jimmy stealing. He grabbed Jimmy by the shirt, pushed him to the ground and stepped on his back until Jimmy was screaming from the pain. The owner pulled out a gun and shoved its barrel against Jimmy's head. He threatened to kill Jimmy if he ever came in the store again. He then threw him out the door and onto the sidewalk.

Jimmy scrambled to his feet and ran as fast as he could. He was so scared he threw up. His back hurt for a week and he could still feel the gun barrel pushing against his head. He stopped stealing, for awhile.

One time, the owner of a store caught Jimmy stealing...

By the time Jimmy got into high school, he had stealing down to a science. He and his friends would go into a store and decide what they wanted. They would wait a few days and then go back. Three of them would create a diversion in one part of the store while the fourth would take the desired merchandise and run out. The others would follow, laughing.

They would sell the stolen items for cash on the street or try to pawn them. Jimmy used his portion to buy weed, and then he graduated to pills. His habit grew until he needed more than his petty theft could support.

To help pay for his drugs, he would steal from his parents. He'd go into his mom's wallet and take some of her money. Once he stole some cash that his dad had stashed away, but it still wasn't enough.

Jimmy's grades were getting so bad that his parents were called into school. His father yelled at him and his mother cried. He was transferred to a special school because he couldn't keep up with the other students.

By now, Jimmy wore a big safety pin through his lip with another one through his nose. One night after snorting some cocaine, Jimmy had his friends pierce his tongue. The pain was excruciating. When he got home, he passed out. Fortunately his dad heard him fall and came to check on him. Jimmy's tongue was bleeding profusely so his dad rushed him to the emergency room. The next day his tongue was swollen so big it wouldn't fit in his mouth properly.

While he was in the hospital, Jimmy's blood test came back positive for drugs. When his parents found out, they made him go to Narcotics Anonymous meetings. Jimmy thought the whole thing was a joke, but he had to convince his parents that he was interested or he would never get out of the house. Usually, he would leave for a meeting, but would end up at his friend's house instead.

When his parents found out he wasn't attending the meetings, they sent him to live at a rehab. He quickly ran away. By the age of seventeen, he was living with friends, or he would crash on the street. When things got really bad, he would call his parents and they would let him come home. He would stay for a night, take what he could to hock, and leave.

One of Jimmy's friends showed him how to burglarize homes. He could steal more from homes than from stores and it felt like there was less chance of getting caught.

Jimmy also found a house that was vacant and moved in. The grass was brown and unmowed and the "For Sale" sign looked as if it had been there for awhile. Jimmy would enter at night, careful the neighbors didn't see him. He would hide what he stole in the attic of the house. He figured it was a safe place to stash the loot, and it was convenient to retrieve when he needed to sell it. The house was also a great place for he and his friends to hang out.

One day, Natasha, one of Jimmy's friends, was arrested for possession of cocaine. The police told her she was going to jail. Her attorney was able to negotiate a deal where Natasha would turn in someone else and receive a lesser sentence. Natasha had been to Jimmy's house and knew about the stolen items. She told the police about Jimmy.

The police had been searching for someone who had been committing a string of burglaries, but no suspects had turned up. They used Natasha's information to obtain an arrest warrant for Jimmy and a search warrant for the vacant house where he was living. After they arrested Jimmy, it didn't take them long to find the hidden loot.

Two days after his eighteenth birthday, Jimmy was charged with twelve residential burglaries. Many of the people whose homes had been burglarized were able to identify items that that the police had found. Two people were able to pick Jimmy out of a lineup. They identified him as the person who had been loitering around their neighborhoods on the days when their homes had been burglarized. Although the burglaries had been committed before Jimmy turned eighteen, he was charged as an adult.

Jimmy's parents were devastated. They wanted to help so they hired a private attorney for Jimmy at a cost of $15,000. After months of negotiating with the District Attorney, Jimmy's lawyer was able to get him a year in the county jail. The D.A. and the Judge agreed that his age was a factor in giving him a lenient sentence. However, he had to enter a guilty plea to eight of the burglaries.

Each of the burglary convictions was considered a strike. Jimmy's attorney talked to him about what that would mean in the future. If he were ever convicted of another felony, the burglaries could be used against him to enhance his sentence. Jimmy would spend twenty-five years to life in prison for any future felony he might commit.

Jimmy pled guilty to the eight residential burglaries. The Judge accepted his plea and explained to him that any new felony would put him in state prison for the rest of his life. Jimmy told the Judge he would never be in trouble again.

When Jimmy was released from jail, he went to live with his parents. The Judge had ordered Jimmy to participate in drug counseling and to get a job or return to school. Jimmy figured the Judge wouldn't mind if he took a few weeks off before starting the program. The few weeks turned into a few months. Jimmy never seemed able to start the drug program or find a job. As a result, his probation officer found him in violation of his probation and Jimmy was ordered to appear in court. Jimmy was scared and ignored the order.

One night, Jimmy and a friend were sitting in a graveyard smoking a joint when the police pulled up. They ran Jimmy's name and found an arrest warrant

Jimmy figured the Judge wouldn't mind if he took a few weeks off before starting drug counseling and looking for a job.

for failure to comply with the terms and conditions of probation. Jimmy was arrested.

A few days later Jimmy was brought before the Judge who had taken his plea on the burglary cases. Jimmy cried and asked for another chance. The Judge told him he'd had his chance and sentenced him to state prison for two years.

Jimmy was released after serving one year. It was the scariest time of his life. Every night he would tell himself that he would never do drugs again. He would promise himself he would get a job and stay out of trouble.

When he was released from prison, his parents wouldn't let him live at home. They helped him with the deposit and first month's rent on an apartment.

To Jimmy, it felt great to be free and in his own apartment. He invited a few friends over to celebrate. There was lots of beer and drugs. One of his friends left a bindle of methamphetamine. Jimmy didn't spot it among the beer bottles and potato chip wrappers.

The next morning, Jimmy's parole officer showed up at his apartment to see how he was doing. The parole officer spotted the package of methamphetamine and placed Jimmy under arrest. He was booked for Possession of a Controlled Substance, a felony, and placed in a cell. A detective came to talk to Jimmy. Jimmy tried to explain that the drugs weren't his. He told the detective that he had a party and someone else must have left the meth there.

Jimmy was brought into court a few days later to be arraigned on the possession charge. He figured his parents would hire a private attorney. Once the Judge knew what was going on, the charges would be dropped and he would be a free man again. He sat in the holding cell and waited.

Later, a Public Defender came to talk to him about his case. She told Jimmy that he had been charged with possession as a felony. She explained that the prosecutor was charging Jimmy with prior strikes and if he were found guilty he would face a mandatory twenty-five years-to-life in prison.

Jimmy tried to explain that he was innocent. The Public Defender said it didn't matter who the drugs belonged to — they were found in his apartment and that's all that counted. Besides, how he was going to prove the drugs weren't his? He said he was sure his friend would come forward to claim the drugs. The Public Defender shook her head. She asked Jimmy if he really believed that his friend would come forward knowing he would face prosecution. Jimmy was arraigned and the next court date was set.

Jimmy was panicked. He called his parents. His mom answered and he yelled at her. He wanted to know why she hadn't been in court and why she hadn't hired an attorney for him. Jimmy told her that he was facing twenty-five years to life in prison. He could hear his mother crying. She explained that they didn't have the money to pay for another attorney. Jimmy's sister had started her first year of college, and the last of their savings had gone to pay for her tuition. Jimmy hung up on her.

Jimmy's parents came to see him on visiting day, but he refused to see them. They came to the courtroom on his next court date, but he refused to acknowledge them. They even contacted the public defender and asked what they could do to help.

The P.D. said that the case would go to trial, unless the prosecutor offered a deal. She explained that it was unlikely.

Jimmy's case did go to trial. He was found guilty of Possession of a Controlled Substance. The Judge sentenced Jimmy to a mandatory term of twenty-five years to life. At the sentencing, the Judge explained to Jimmy that he would not be eligible for parole for twenty years. Jimmy was nineteen-years-old.

The Law

HABITUAL OFFENDER
Criminal Statute Section 22000

A person is considered an habitual offender if he or she has been convicted of a serious or violent felony in this state, or in any other state, and is then convicted of another felony. The sentence of an habitual offender will be enhanced by doubling the term of imprisonment of the subsequent felony.

SERIOUS & VIOLENT OFFENSES
Criminal Statute Section 22002

The following crimes are considered serious and violent felonies:

1. Murder

2. Kidnapping

3. Manslaughter

4. Robbery

6. Residential robbery

7. Arson

8. Carjacking

9. Use of a dangerous or deadly weapon during the commission of a felony

10. Selling a controlled substance to a minor

11. Rape

THIRD FELONY CONVICTION
("THIRD STRIKE LAW")
Criminal Statute Section 22000

Any person who has previously been convicted of two serious or violent felonies in this state or any other state, and suffers a conviction of a third felony, shall serve a mandatory sentence of twenty-five years to life in prison.

Since the laws in each state are different, the laws cited in this book may not reflect those in your state.

Questions

1. How many years will Jimmy serve in prison?

In the state where Jimmy lives, he will serve at least 20 years of his sentence before he is eligible to be paroled. A parole board will then talk to Jimmy to determine if he should be released. If the board decides to deny parole, Jimmy could serve even more time, up to the rest of his life.

2. Do all states have 'strike' laws?

More than thirty states have 'strike' laws that require mandatory, long term prison sentences for habitual offenders.

3. Does the "Third Strike Law" apply to minors?

A minor who is tried in the juvenile court system cannot be sentenced according to the "Third Strike Law." That means he won't be sent to prison for 25-years-to-life. However, a minor who is convicted of a 'strikable' offense does receive a strike on his record that will enhance any future sentences he may receive as an adult.

Although Jimmy had committed the burglaries before he turned eighteen, he was charged as an adult and the convictions counted as strikes against him.

In many states, convictions in juvenile court of serious or violent offenses can be used to enhance a future felony conviction received as an adult.

4. How long can a minor be kept in custody?

In most states, a minor can only be charged and convicted as a juvenile until the age of seventeen. However, in most states, a minor can be imprisoned by the juvenile court until he or she is twenty-one years of age. In California, a minor can be imprisoned until the age of twenty-five.

5. If a minor is convicted as an adult, would the minor go to adult prison?

In some states, he would be imprisoned in the juvenile prison system until he is eighteen years of age. Then he would be transferred to the adult prison system to finish his term. In other states, he would be placed in the adult prison system from the moment he was convicted, no matter what his age.

Chapter 9
Anthony

When Anthony was eight, he could hardly wait until he was old enough to be jumped into the local gang. As soon as he came home from school, he was out the door to the local hangout where he would smoke, drink and run errands for the gang members. Anthony would beam as the gang members playfully ruffled his hair and referred to him as their mascot.

"When can I become a member?"

"When you're old enough to show that you're made of the right stuff. You gotta prove yourself."

"How do I prove myself?"

"You gotta show us you're a man."

By the time he was ten, the members of the gang were sending Anthony on "missions" — transporting money and narcotics, and acting as a lookout. They figured the police wouldn't suspect such a little kid. They were right. After completing his missions, the older guys would congratulate him.

When Anthony turned twelve, he was approached by Henry, one of the leaders.

"It's time you showed us what you're made off. Time to be a man."

"What do I have to do?" Anthony asked.

"49th Street is having a meeting today. We need to take them out. You in?"

"I'm in," said Anthony.

"They aren't going to suspect you," Henry said.

He handed Anthony a loaded nine-millimeter gun.

"This will fire eleven bullets. That should be enough. You and Philip are going to ride by on a bike. Philip will be steering. You'll be sitting on the bar. Don't look at them as you ride up. You don't want to draw their attention and you don't want them to identify you. Keep the gun hidden until you get really close, then pull it out and fire. Just keep firing until you use up all the bullets. Jerry will be waiting around the corner with the car. Okay?"

"Yeah," Anthony answered.

"When this is done, you're one of us."

Henry patted Anthony on the back. A few hours later, Philip came by with the bike.

"Let's go."

Anthony hopped on with the gun tucked in the waistband of his pants. They rode several blocks out of their territory, into the 49th Street territory where the rival gang was meeting. As they came around the corner, Anthony saw a group of people standing around in front of a house. Music was blaring. People were talking and laughing. As they got close, Anthony pulled out the gun. His hands were trembling. He closed his eyes and pulled the trigger once, twice... until the chamber was empty.

"You and Philip are going to ride by on a bike... Keep the gun hidden until you get really close, then pull it out and fire."

Philip pedaled around the corner. They jumped off the bike, leapt into the car and sped off.

Anthony was sweating and shaking.

"Did I get any of them?"

"I don't know, man, but they sure ran like rabbits when you started firing."

They went back to the place where Henry was waiting.

"Anthony unloaded all the rounds into them!"

Henry nodded.

"Good work, Anthony. Did you make contact with any of them? Did you see any of them go down?"

"I don't know, boss, but it seems like it."

That night the gang celebrated its newest member. Beer and liquor flowed freely. Music played, people laughed, everything was good.

The next day Anthony met up with the others.

"Any news?"

Nobody said a word. Henry threw a folded newspaper to Anthony.

"Front Page."

Anthony opened the paper and looked. The President wanted to cut taxes. Gas prices were up. Then he saw it.

"Yesterday Monique Jenkins, age 2, was shot to death by an unknown assailant. Three others were wounded, including an elderly woman who was shot in the head.

She is in critical condition. The assailant remains at large. Witnesses identified him as a young male with dark hair, possibly 12 or 13 years of age."

Henry shook his head.

"You weren't supposed to shoot an old lady and a young kid."

"I did what you said. I fired all the bullets into the group."

"You were supposed to get the 49th Street Gang, not somebody's grandmother and a young kid."

Henry shook his head again.

"We'll have to call a special meeting. There's gonna be retaliation."

Suddenly, the police closed in before the gang knew what hit them. Everyone was taken to the station. Anthony, Philip and several other members were placed in separate interview rooms. Soon, a large man entered the room where Anthony was sitting.

"My name is Detective Fulgoni. I've been assigned to investigate the death of Monique Jenkins. Anything you wanna tell me?"

"I don't know a thing about it."

"You sure that's the story you wanna stick by?"

"Yup."

Detective Fulgoni left the room. Anthony sat there for what seemed like hours before Fulgoni returned.

"Can I go now?" Anthony asked.

"Shut up. Your friends just ratted you out, homeboy. They're singing like little birds. They say you're the one who fired the gun. How's it feel to be a baby killer?"

Anthony sat silently.

"Okay, Big Man — when you go to prison you can tell your cellmates that you're a baby killer."

Another officer came in the interview room.

"I just came from talking to Monique's mom. Monique was her only baby. She can't have anymore babies."

The officer threw a stack of 8 x 10 photographs on the table in front of Anthony.

"Take a look at these, Big Man."

He spread them out in front of Anthony.

Anthony gazed at the pictures. He saw the little girl lying lifeless on the ground. He could see where the bullets had entered her body. The weight of what he had done began to dawn on him. Tears started to roll down his face.

"Okay, Anthony. Why don't you tell us what happened."

Detective Fulgoni read Anthony his rights. The other officer set up a video camera. Anthony waived his rights and told them the whole story. He explained how he had fired the gun.

Two days later, a hearing was held to determine whether Anthony should be tried as a juvenile or as an adult. The Judge listened to the attorneys and decided that Anthony should be tried as an adult.

"You might be a child of 13, but your actions were not those of a child. A child couldn't do what you did. This crime required thought, premeditation and sophistication in its planning. Therefore, I will grant the District Attorney's request to file against you as an adult."

"Anthony, it is the court's finding that you are to stand trial as an adult. The crimes you are accused of committing were heinous and callous, with no thought for human life. Your case will be transferred to adult court forthwith."

The D.A. stood up.

"Your honor, I have with me a copy of the complaint filed against the defendant for one count of Murder, one count of Attempted Murder and four counts of Assault With a Deadly Weapon. Bail is set in the amount of $500,000. Because of his age, the defendant is not eligible for the death penalty, but the District Attorney's office will be seeking Life In Prison Without Parole."

The Law

JUVENILE STATUTE SECTION 56.8

Waiver of Juvenile To Adult Court For Criminal Proceeding

A minor who has attained the age of 12 will be tried as an adult for the following offenses:

1. Robbery with personal use of a firearm

2. Rape

3. Kidnapping

4. Discharging a weapon into an inhabited house

5. Escape from juvenile hall, boot camp, or any other kind of placement where injury is intentionally inflicted on an employee of the juvenile facility during the escape

6. Manufacturing or selling 1/2 ounce or more of an illegal narcotic

7. Attempted Murder

8. Murder

9. Manslaughter

10. Carjacking

Since the laws in each state are different, the laws cited in this book may not reflect those in your state.

Questions

1. Anthony was only thirteen. How could he be tried as an adult?

In the state where Anthony lives, the law allows a minor over the age of twelve to be tried as an adult for certain serious crimes. The Judge decided Anthony's crime was too violent for him to benefit from rehabilitation in the juvenile system. As a result, his case was transferred to adult court.

2. What does life in prison without parole mean?

It means you never get out of prison. If Anthony is convicted and sentenced to Life Without Parole (L-WOP), he will spend from age thirteen until his death in prison with no possibility of release.

3. Do you think a thirteen-year-old child who commits a serious crime should be put in prison for life, or have a chance at rehabilitation?

Statistics

Twenty-seven states do not have a minimum age at which a child can be tried as an adult.

Chapter 10
Marty

Marty was an average student who was more interested in playing football and partying than in studying. He was the quarterback of his high school football team and had tons of friends.

At sixteen, Marty went to work for his dad part-time and made good money. Life was great. Every weekend was a party with lots of beer and lots of fun.

When he was seventeen, Marty's mom and dad helped him buy a truck. He got a speeding ticket the first month he had it. His mom was mad, but his dad said it was just a guy thing and told her not to worry. Marty paid the fine and took care of the ticket.

A few months later, Marty got another ticket. This time, it was for Exhibitionist Speeding. Marty and a friend wanted to see whose truck was faster, so they pealed out from a light and sped right past a police car.

The Judge told Marty, "Next time you get a ticket, you'll lose your driving privileges until you are twenty-one-years-old."

Marty's parents took the truck away and told him he would have to work hard to regain their trust. The only place they would drive him to was school or to sporting events. If he wanted to go anywhere else, he had to ask his girlfriend, Anne, to take him.

Marty and Anne were planning to get married after high school. She nagged him about his drinking, but he told her he knew what he was doing.

Marty applied himself more at school and his grades began to improve. He drank less and tried to do more chores at home.

The next semester, Marty's grades were up and his parents gave him back his truck. That was the best day — freedom at last! Marty tried to limit his drinking, but he started partying on the weekends again.

At the end of the semester, Marty and his friends planned a senior camping trip. They were going to the river to camp out for a couple of days. Marty's mom and dad agreed to let him go with the understanding that he would call everyday and there was to be absolutely no drinking.

When the day of the trip arrived, Marty drove Anne and his best friend Mark up to the river. They pitched a couple of tents and built a fire. The guys decided to rough it and sleep under the stars.

On Saturday, they swam in the river and floated on inner tubes. Everyone had a great time. That night there was a big bash. Marty had so much to drink that he passed-out next to the campfire.

The next morning, Marty woke up with his face in the dirt. Mark was already awake and had an open beer in his hand. He handed it to Marty and told him

Marty tried to limit his drinking, but he started partying on the weekends again.

that drinking it would help him feel better. Marty drank up, but still felt terrible.

A few minutes later, they heard Anne cry out. She was barefoot and had stepped on a broken beer bottle. Her foot was bleeding badly. They wrapped it in a towel, but the blood continued to seep. They decided to drive her to a doctor.

Marty's head was spinning as they started down the mountain road. Each new turn in the road made him feel even worse. He finally came around a corner too fast and lost control of his truck. The truck rolled over twice before coming to rest on its roof.

Marty had hit his head and blacked out for a few minutes. When he came to, he remembered somebody trying to help him out of the truck. He passed out again.

When Marty finally regained consciousness, he was in a hospital room. His parents were there and his mom was crying. His dad told him that he had been hurt pretty badly and that his pelvis had been smashed.

The next day when Marty woke up, he started asking about Anne and Mark. Every time he asked, the nurse would look away and tell him to discuss it with the doctor. When the doctor came in, Marty asked again. He was told that Mark was fine – a few cuts and bruises. But Anne had been thrown from the truck. She had received severe head trauma and was in a coma. The doctor said that if she survived, she would probably have brain damage. He also said that her face had been badly injured.

Marty was released a few weeks later. Things were pretty bad at home. Nobody talked to him and none of his friends came by. His mom and dad didn't know what to say.

Marty asked if he could visit Anne. Her parents said they didn't want him around her.

A couple of weeks after Marty got home from the hospital, he received a letter from the District Attorney's office notifying him to appear in court. He was being charging with causing injury to another person while under the influence of alcohol. The police had tested his blood at the hospital and it was three times the legal limit for minors.

Marty's dad took him to see a defense attorney who explained that Marty would probably have to do some time in jail. He said things would get a lot worse if Anne died. He also said they would probably be sued by Anne's parents because the cost of her care would be so expensive.

Anne did survive, but she was brain damaged and required constant nursing care. She didn't recognize anyone, not even her parents.

Although Marty was under eighteen, the prosecutor elected to file Marty's case in adult court. Marty pled guilty to a felony charge of Reckless Driving Under the Influence of Alcohol and Causing an Injury. The Judge could have sentenced Marty to state prison, but decided that one year in the county jail was more appropriate.

Once, Marty snuck into Ann's hospital room...

Anne's parents sued Marty's parents in civil court for the cost of her lifetime care. Because Marty wasn't eighteen, his parents were held legally responsible. The jury awarded Anne's parents $8 million.

Marty's parents were forced to sell their home, cars, and all the money they had saved for retirement. In addition, the court ordered them to make monthly payments to Anne's parents out of their salaries.

The Law

RECKLESS DRIVING UNDER THE INFLUENCE OF
ALCOHOL OR DRUGS AND CAUSING BODILY INJURY
Vehicle Code Section 48

Any person who, while under the influence of alcohol or drugs, drives a vehicle in a reckless manner which causes injury to another person is in violation of Vehicle Code Section 48.

A violation of Vehicle Code Section 48 is punishable by up to one year in the county jail or imprisonment in the state prison for 16 months, 2 years or 3 years.

Since the laws in each state are different, the laws cited in this book may not reflect those in your state.

Questions

1. What is the difference between jail and prison?

Prisons are operated by the state. Prisons house inmates who have been convicted of serious crimes.

Jails are generally run by a city or county. Usually, two types of defendants are housed in a county jail — those awaiting trial who cannot post their bail and those who have been convicted of a misdemeanor. Some people who have been convicted of felonies are also allowed to serve in county jail instead of prison.

People who are convicted of misdemeanors do not go to state prison. Only someone who has been convicted of a felony can receive a sentence that includes time in state prison.

2. Does the Judge have to send a person to prison when he is found guilty of a felony?

It depends. For some felony convictions, the law allows the judge a choice of sentencing the defendant to state prison or to county jail.

3. Could the Judge have sent Marty to state prison?

Yes. Marty was very lucky that the Judge only sentenced him to county jail. Marty pleaded to a felony that carried a minimum sentence of 16 months, a mid-term sentence of 2 years and a high term of 3 years. The Judge could have sentenced Marty to any of the terms in state prison, or to county jail.

Statistics

There are approximately 9.5 million drinkers between the ages twelve to twenty. Of that number, 1.9 million are heavy drinkers.

Teenagers who began drinking by age fifteen are four times more likely to develop alcohol addiction than those who begin drinking at age twenty-one.

Chapter II
Kevin

Kevin lived with his mother. He had never known his father, although he spent much of his time daydreaming about him. He had asked his mother countless times about his dad, but each time she would either tell him he was better off not knowing or she would get angry with Kevin for asking. When Kevin was ten, his mother told him not to ask about his father ever again. After that, Kevin spent even more time dreaming about his dad. Sometimes his dad was a war hero who was killed by an evil enemy. Sometimes he was an undercover agent like James Bond, who couldn't reveal he was Kevin's father because it would put Kevin and his mother in danger.

By the time Kevin was twelve he no longer dreamed of a Dad. Instead, he started to think about drugs. A friend of his mother's had turned him onto marijuana. He shared joints with Kevin and supplied him with marijuana in exchange for errands.

Kevin liked the feeling he got from being high. It helped him forget about his troubles. Soon, Kevin was sampling hard drugs like speed and cocaine. To pay for the drugs, he would sometimes take cash out of his mother's wallet. Other times he would steal items from the corner store and sell them on the street.

One of the dealers Kevin bought drugs from was the same age as himself. He told Kevin he could pay for his habit and have money in his pocket if he would start selling dope.

By the time he was fourteen, Kevin had moved from using to selling. Each night, he was out on the corner dealing drugs. People came to him and gave him money. They needed him and he felt invincible.

Sometimes Kevin had problems with other dealers running him off his corner. On a couple of occasions, they jumped him and took his drugs, so he bought a gun to protect himself.

It was easy enough to purchase a gun on the street. He met with an acquaintance, gave him some money and purchased a handgun. He kept the gun tucked in the waistband of his pants, hidden from view by his baggy shirt.

Jake was one of Kevin's former customers. Rumor had it that he had just been suspended from college for drug use. His parents had sent him to a drug rehab, but Jake walked out after the first day. Jake didn't have money, and he kept hoping to score free dope.

When Kevin saw Jake coming towards him he started to walk away. But Jake got down on his knees and pleaded for drugs. Kevin shoved him, but Jake grabbed the leg of his pants.

"I'll pay you tomorrow, I promise."

"Stop bothering me," Kevin yelled and kicked Jake away.

Kevin saw a couple of guys he knew. They went behind a building and smoked some crack cocaine. As they walked out to the street, Jake came up to Kevin

The more desperate Jake behaved, the more it irritated Kevin.

once more and asked for dope. Kevin pushed him away. Jake fell and started to cry.

"Can't you see, I'm sick and need a fix?"

The more desperate Jake behaved, the more it irritated Kevin.

"Later," Kevin said.

Kevin ran a few blocks and found a corner where he could open up shop. The corner was slow. He was angry at Jake and felt himself seething inside.

He was finally negotiating a sale when Jake found him again. It was Kevin's first sale since moving to the new corner. Jake started tugging at his sleeve.

"Please help me."

Kevin shoved him aside and snapped, "Get away from me."

The buyer started to look around nervously. Kevin tried to reassure him.

"It's okay, he's just crazy. Don't worry about him."

Kevin and his customer continued to discuss price.

"Come on, man. I'm really hurtin'. You gotta help me."

Jake was shaking all over. Kevin grabbed Jake and pulled him a few feet away.

"Get away from me, or you'll be sorry."

"You got to help me. Please give me a hit," Jake begged.

Kevin turned back to his customer just in time to see him walking off.

"Hey, wait..."

The customer looked around nervously.

"This doesn't feel right. I'm taking my business elsewhere."

Kevin could feel his temper boiling. He walked into a dark alley and motioned for Jake to follow. Jake felt relieved, thinking he was finally going to get his fix. When Jake was a few feet away, Kevin grabbed the gun out of his waistband. He pointed it at Jake and pulled the trigger.

Several neighbors heard the shot. They could see Kevin running from the ally. They knew him and were tired of him selling drugs in front of their houses. They called the police and hoped he would be arrested.

After the shooting, Kevin ran home. His mother was at work, and he sat on his bed holding the gun in his hands. The enormity of what he had done began to settle on him. What if Jake died? What should he do?

He ran outside and buried the gun in the trash can. He took off his clothes and threw them in his closet. He went into the bathroom and wiped the splattered blood off his hands and face. He crawled into bed and pulled the covers over his head.

An hour later, Kevin heard a crash. Before he could sit up, five police officers burst into the room with guns drawn. Two of them yanked him out of bed and threw him face down on the floor. One of the officers knelt on Kevin's back while the other handcuffed him. He was grabbed by the hair and dragged out of the room. One of the officers started reading information from a card.

"You have the right to remain silent..."

Kevin was shoved into the back of a police cruiser. Two officers got into the front and the car sped off.

"Where are you taking me?"

Where do you think we're taking you?" the officer said sarcastically. "You're under arrest."

Kevin was taken to the juvenile detention center and booked into custody. He was stripped of his clothes and body-searched. He was given a jail uniform and his mug shot and fingerprints were taken. An officer did a gun residue test on Kevin's hands and arms, as well as on the clothes they found in his closet. They also tested his clothes for blood spatters.

Kevin was placed in a cell and left to sit. At dinner-time, an officer brought a tray into the cell, but left without saying anything. A few hours later, Kevin was taken to an interview room. A man in a suit was waiting.

"I'm Detective Esposito. I'd like to talk to you, but first I'm going to read you your rights. I'm going to record your responses. Okay?"

"Yeah."

"You have the right to remain silent. If you give up that right, anything you say can be used against you in a court of law? Do you understand that right?"

"Yeah."

"Do you give up that right?"

"Yeah."

"You have the right to an attorney. If you can't afford an attorney, one will be appointed for you. Do you understand that right?"

"Yeah."

"Do you give up that right?"

"Yeah."

"Kevin, will you talk to me?"

"Okay."

"I'm going to record our conversation, okay?"

Kevin nodded his head.

"Is that a yes?"

"Yeah."

"Do you know Jacob Garretti?"

"I know a guy named Jake."

"Did you see Jake earlier today?"

"Yeah."

"Did you sell drugs to Jake tonight?"

"No."

"Kevin, I've got four witnesses who place you selling drugs to Jake today. Don't lie to me."

"He didn't have any money, so I didn't sell him anything. He just kept hanging around and bothering me."

"We found the gun you used in a trash can outside your house. We're testing it for your fingerprints right now. Did you throw the gun in the trash?"

"Yeah."

"Is that the gun you used to shoot Jake?"

"Yeah. How is he?"

"He's dead."

Detective Esposito questioned Kevin for more than two hours, walking through what had happened, and how and why Kevin had shot Jake.

At the end of the interview, Detective Esposito told Kevin, "You're being charged with the murder of Jacob Garretti."

Kevin was taken back to his cell. He sat there alone, wondering if his mother knew and what she would think. He wondered what would happen next.

For two nights, Kevin sat in his cell. No one talked to him, no one even looked at him. Another inmate brought him food and left. Occasionally, he heard other people talking, but they never came close enough to the cell door for him to see. With each passing hour, Kevin became more and more frightened. Sometimes he cried, sometimes he raged around the cell, punching the walls. Once, an officer told him to quiet down. Kevin asked what was going to happen to him? The officer left without answering.

On the morning of the third day, an officer yelled into the cell.

"Wake up. Time to go to court."

About an hour later, the officer came back and unlocked the cell door.

"Turn around and put your hands behind your back."

He snapped hand cuffs on Kevin.

The officer walked Kevin through a maze of hall-ways. Whenever they came to a door, the officer would yell, "Face to the wall. Don't move." He would push Kevin face first into the wall, keeping the palm of his hand on Kevin's back while he unlocked the door with his other hand.

After being pushed through a series of doors, Kevin was finally escorted into a courtroom. There he saw his mother sitting in the back of the room. She had dark circles under her eyes. Kevin was shocked at how old she looked. When she saw Kevin, she started to cry. Kevin turned to say something to his mother, but the officer pushed him into a chair and shoved his shoulder forward.

"No talking allowed."

A man sitting in the next chair introduced himself as the Public Defender. He explained to Kevin that he had been charged with murder and that a hearing was being held to determine if Kevin should be tried as a juvenile or as an adult.

Kevin sat with his head down. People he didn't know got on the witness stand and testified against him. After they were finished, the Judge spoke to Kevin.

"Kevin Hargrove, you have been charged with the crime of murder. Taking into consideration the serious-ness of the crime, your age, and the circumstances surrounding the crime, it is my determination that you are to be transferred to the jurisdiction of the adult criminal court to stand trial."

The Public Defender turned to Kevin, "Your case is being sent to adult court. You'll be taken to the adult detention center to await your Arraignment."

"What's an Arraignment?" Kevin asked.

"That's where they tell you what you've been charged with, and you enter a plea."

"Will you be there?" Kevin asked.

"No. A Public Defender from the adult court will represent you."

An officer pulled Kevin out of the chair and led him away. Kevin turned towards his mother, but all he saw was her back as she went out the courtroom door.

Kevin was taken to a different cell and handcuffed to a bench.

"A bus from men's jail will be here in a few hours to pick you up," the officer said.

Kevin sat for three hours. Finally, an officer uncuffed him from the bench and recuffed his hands behind him. He pulled out another pair of cuffs and attached them to Kevin's ankles.

"What are you doing?" Kevin asked.

"You're an accused murderer. Standard operating procedure," the officer told Kevin. "Take shorter steps so you don't trip."

Kevin was transported to the men's jail where he was processed. He was searched and given a different jail uniform.

There were no windows at the men's jail. Everything was made of cement and steel. Kevin was placed in a ten-by-twenty-foot cell with five other inmates, All of them were much bigger and older than Kevin.

The cell walls were cement on three sides and the fourth wall was made of thick metal wire with a heavy metal door. A set of bunks, stacked three high, were along two of the walls. The back wall had a toilet and a sink. Kevin noticed that the toilet was less than three feet from the bunks. Kevin was scared as he had never been scared before.

"Those Nike shoes?" One of the inmates asked Kevin after the guard walked away.

"Yeah."

"Give me your shoes."

"What?"

"You deaf? Give me your shoes."

"No. These are my shoes. If I give them to you, I won't have any," Kevin said.

"Wouldn't that be too bad," the inmate said with a menacing smile.

Kevin climbed on the empty bunk, trying to ignore the man. He lay on his back and closed his eyes. Suddenly, he was yanked off the bunk and his head hit the cement floor. Someone rolled him on his stomach

Kevin was scared as he had never been scared before.

and grabbed him around the neck. He gasped for breath. He tried to yell but the hands tightened around his neck. He was face down and couldn't see who was on top of him. He felt his shoes being ripped off his feet. Whoever was holding him let go. He rolled over, choking and trying to catch his breath. His head was bleeding. He began to cry.

"You're bad. Real tough," one of the inmates said while the others laughed.

Kevin looked over at the man who was now wearing his shoes. He started swearing. They all laughed again.

"Better shut up before Vince comes over there and gives you a real pounding."

One of the others jumped down off his bunk and looked at Kevin's head.

"You'll live. If the guard asks, you hit your head by accident. You won't like it here much if you say any-thing. If you do talk, don't count on being here long."

Kevin crawled over to the sink. He watched the water turn red as he washed away the blood. His hands were shaking. He took some toilet paper and held it to the cut. After a few minutes, he crawled back to his bunk.

The men in the cell continued to terrorize Kevin. They constantly took advantage of him. There wasn't a moment when he wasn't scared. They were locked in the cell twenty-three hours a day and let out one hour a day for exercise. Meals were brought to the cell by another inmate, who slid the trays through a hole in the door. The others would take food off Kevin's tray, leaving him with whatever they didn't want.

His mother came to visit him once a week, but that made him feel even worse. He was allowed a twenty minute visit with her. A thick piece of plexiglass separated Kevin from his mother. They were able to talk by a phone located on either side of the glass. She would cry over the new cuts and bruises he had acquired. She would blame herself and ask Kevin where she had gone wrong.

Each month, Kevin would go to court. After his second appearance in adult court, his attorney came to visit.

"You are charged with murder, and the prosecutors are seeking the death penalty."

"You mean I could be killed?" Kevin asked in disbelief.

"Yes."

Kevin sat staring off into space.

"At least it would get me out of here."

"Are you having problems here?"

"Like you could do anything."

"I could speak with the watch commander."

Kevin was suddenly afraid.

"No. Please don't say anything," Kevin pleaded. "If you do, it'll be worse for me. Don't do me any favors."

His attorney nodded. The trial date for Kevin's case was set to begin two days after his seventeenth birthday. On the day of the trial, his mother brought regular clothes for him to wear. He sat next to his attorney and watched as a jury was selected and the testimony began.

Two neighbors testified, identifying Kevin as the person who ran out of the alley after they had heard the shot. Another testified that he had seen Kevin with Jake a few minutes before the shooting. The medical examiner testified that Jake had been killed by a twenty-five caliber bullet. A police expert testified that the bullet taken out of Jake's body had been fired from the twenty-five caliber gun found with Kevin's fingerprints on it.

The jury deliberated for two days before coming back with a verdict. They found Kevin guilty of first degree murder.

His attorney explained that there would be a second part of the trial — the penalty phase. The jury would now decide the separate issue of how Kevin should be punished, by life in prison or death. The D.A. presented negative evidence about Kevin and his character. Kevin's attorney presented positive evidence.

The jury deliberated again, only this time it took just four hours. Their verdict — death. Kevin heard his mother scream.

After the trial, Kevin's attorney came to see him and explained that he would soon be transferred to a penitentiary. He told Kevin that his case would be assigned to an appeals attorney. By law, Kevin's case would be appealed. He explained that the appeal process was automatic because he had received the death penalty sentence.

A week later, Kevin was transferred to a state penitentiary where he was placed in a special cell block for inmates who had been sentenced to death. He was given a cell all to himself. He was allowed to exercise one hour a day outside of the cell, but even then it was by himself. The guards didn't talk to him much. He didn't see any of the other inmates. He had no one to talk to. He spent hours lying on his bunk dreaming about his life before he had shot Jake. He would often cry over the loss of his freedom. He knew he would never get to do the things that other people took for granted. He couldn't go to the movies. He would never ride around in a car with the windows down and the breeze blowing in. He would never get to hug his mom again or hang out on the corner with his friends. All he had to look forward to was this cell, for the rest of his life, however long that would be.

The Law

MURDER

Criminal Statute Section 433

Murder is the unlawful killing of a human being with malice, premeditation and deliberation. Malice is when someone tries to injure another person, either intentionally or with wanton disregard for human safety.

1ST DEGREE MURDER

Any murder which is premeditated and deliberate is 1st degree murder. Premeditation is when someone thinks about what they are going to do. Deliberation is when someone weighs the consequences of the action.

2ND DEGREE MURDER

2nd degree murder is any murder that does not rise to the level of 1st degree murder.

Since the laws in each state are different, the laws cited in this book may not reflect those in your state.

Questions

1. How is a person tried for 1st degree murder?

Anyone who deliberately kills someone and thought about the act and the consequences ahead of time, even if for only two seconds, will be charged with 1st degree murder.

In states that have the death penalty, the trial is divided into two parts. The first part is the guilt phase, where the jury determines if the defendant is guilty of first degree murder.

If the defendant is found guilty, then there is a second part of the trial where the jury decides what the punishment should be — either the death penalty or life in prison without parole.

In all other trials, except for 1st degree murder, the jury decides on the issue of guilt, but the Judge decides the punishment. Caveat: Not all states require the Jury to determine the punishment in a 1st degree case. Some states have a panel of Judges who decide. Other states allow the trial Judge to decide.

2. If Kevin had been tried and convicted as a juvenile, would he still have received the death penalty?

No. A death penalty sentence is an adult punishment. A minor tried and convicted in a juvenile court can not be sentenced to death.

3. How does a jury work? What's a "hung jury?"

A jury in an adult criminal trial is made up of twelve people (Only a few states allow less than twelve people on a jury in a criminal case). After the jury has heard all the evidence, the Judge instructs them about the law. Then they deliberate. This means they discuss the case among themselves and decide their verdict. All jurors must agree for there to be a verdict. In other words, all twelve jurors must have voted guilty or all twelve jurors must have voted not guilty.

If the jurors have tried to reach a verdict, but are unable to agree, the Judge can declare a hung jury. (They are literally "hung up" on reaching a verdict.) If the Judge believes the jury will not be able to reach an unanimous agreement, the jury will be dismissed and the Judge will declare a mistrial. The D.A. can then re-try the case with a new jury or choose not to refile the case.

4. What are alternate jurors?

When a jury is selected, one or more alternate jurors are often included in addition to the original twelve jurors. Alternate jurors listen to the entire trial with the other jurors, only they don't vote unless one of the original twelve jurors is unable to continue serving and is excused by the Judge.

Statistics

In twenty states the minimum age for the death penalty is sixteen-years-old.

More than sixty men are on death row throughout the US for crimes they committed as juveniles.

Chapter 12
Gary

Gary worked for a hauling company after school. He had been a part time driver for Hendricks Hauling for almost two years. Most of the time he picked up dirt and hauled it to another location.

In addition to hauling dirt, Hendricks Hauling had a contract to pick up chemical waste from local manufacturing plants. They delivered the toxic waste to a special waste disposal area. The cost of disposing the toxic waste was very expensive and Mr. Hendricks was always complaining that he was losing money on the contract.

After Gary graduated from high school, Mr. Hendricks gave him the waste disposal route. Gary was pleased because it included a raise. He had to take a special class in handling toxic waste material and received a special license after completing the class.

Gary had been on the route for almost a year when Mr. Hendricks called him into the office.

"There's had been another increase in the disposal cost."

Gary nodded his head.

"There's another dump site where I want you to take the waste. They charge less."

The next day Gary picked up the waste and took it to the new dump site. When he got to the site, there was a small shack. He went inside.

"I have a drop off from Hendricks."

The man sitting behind the desk looked at the two men standing by the coffee machine.

"Help him get the stuff unloaded."

Gary and the men unloaded the barrels onto the dirt.

"Where's the dump site?" Gary asked looking around.

"Mind your own business," one of the men said.

When Gary returned he told Mr. Hendricks about the new site.

"Don't worry, Gary. Everything's fine out there. Besides, we're not hauling nuclear waste."

After a few months, Gary was approached by the owner of the new dump site.

"How'd you like to make an extra $1,000 a month?"

"What do I have to do for it?" Gary asked.

"Take the barrels up the road a few miles and unload them."

"You want me to just dump this stuff?" Gary asked.

"Look. It's a safe place. No one around for miles. One of the guys will come up later and bury them. Nobody's going to see you. Don't worry."

Gary took the money and transported the barrels to the location which was not far from the river. He unloaded them and left. For the next six months he would bring the barrels up to the spot and unload them. Another man would be waiting to help him.

"Don't worry, Gary. Everything's fine out there."

The barrels would be gone when he returned for the next drop off.

One day Gary noticed a discoloration on the surface of the water. He walked over to the edge of the river. All of the grass and plants had died in a ten foot area around the discoloration. Gary suddenly realized that the barrels were being dumped into the river.

"This river is the water supply for our town," Gary thought. "These chemicals may be getting into our drinking water. But it probably gets diluted and isn't dangerous," he rationalized.

Gary continued delivering the waste for a few more months. After awhile, he became overwhelmed by the ramifications of what he was doing and quit his job at Hendricks hauling.

For months after he quit, Gary worried about what to do. If he told the authorities about the dumping, he might be criminally charged. If he didn't say anything, it was unlikely anyone would ever find out that he'd been involved in the illegal dumping. Gary was afraid he would go to jail, so he didn't say anything. Besides, he thought, those guys must know what they're doing.

Time passed, and Gary tried to forget about the dumping. He married his girlfriend, Karen, and they had two children.

Several years later, his daughter, Amanda, was diagnosed with leukemia. The treatments made her so sick that she couldn't lift her head off the pillow. She lost her hair and was in excruciating pain. Gary was heartbroken to see her little body waste away. He suffered almost as much as she did.

Over the years, the cancer rate in the town began to rise. The local medical community became concerned and started to document the increase. The Environmental Protection Agency sent people to assist. The water supply was tested and found to be contaminated with chemicals that cause cancer. Eventually, the source of the pollution was traced to the illegal dumping site along the bank of the river.

The Law

DUMPING OF TOXIC WASTE
Safety Code Section 3020

Any person who knowingly dumps hazardous waste onto any unauthorized land, or into any river, lake, stream, body of water, or on a shore or bank is guilty of dumping of toxic waste.

The violation of Safety Code Section 3020 is punishable by not more than 1 year in the county jail, or by imprisonment in the state prison for 16 months, 2 years or 3 years, or by a fine of not more than $25,000, or by both fine and imprisonment.

INVOLUNTARY MANSLAUGHTER

Criminal Statute Section 489

The unlawful killing of a human being without malice. Must arise from acting without due caution.

Involuntary manslaughter is punishable by imprisonment in the state prison for 4, 7 or 11 years.

STATUTE OF LIMITATION

Criminal Statute Section 7728

Prosecution for an offense punishable by imprisonment for up to 5 years must begin within 3 years after the commission of the crime.

Prosecution for an offense punishable by imprisonment for 10 years or more must begin within 8 years after the commission of the crime.

Prosecution for an offense punishable by death or imprisonment for life has no statute of limitation.

Since the laws in each state are different, the laws cited in this book may not reflect those in your state.

Questions

1. Is there a statute of limitation on crimes such as "Dumping of Toxic Waste"?

Statutes of limitation vary from state to state, but for most crimes, the case must be filed within a set number of years after the crime was committed. This is called the limitation of action or statute of limitation. The statute limitation for a felony is longer than for a misdemeanor.

There are a few exceptions. There is no statute of limitation for murder.

In Gary's case, the District Attorney's office would have to file within three years of the crime. If more than three years had passed since Gary committed the crime, he cannot be prosecuted for dumping toxic waste.

2. Are there any other criminal charges that could be filed against Gary?

It is possible that he could be charged with involuntary manslaughter. Involuntary manslaughter is when you cause the death of another person without malice but you acted without due caution.

In this case, there would have to be proof that the waste Gary dropped at the riverbank contributed to the deaths in his town.

After reading the facts of this case, do you think that Gary could have been charged with involuntary manslaughter?

3. Even if the D.A.'s office wanted to charge Gary with Involuntary Manslaughter, hasn't the statue of limitations expired?

It depends on how much time has passed. In the state where Gary lives, the maximum sentence for Involuntary Manslaughter is 11 years, which extends the statute of limitations to 10 years. The D.A. would have to investigate and file charges against Gary before the 10 year statute of limitations was up.

4. What's the difference between murder and manslaughter?

Murder requires malice, and premeditation and deliberation. Manslaughter usually involves reckless conduct that results in a death.

Manslaughter is an alternative to murder when the facts usually don't rise to the level of murder.

Legal
Resources

Juvenile And Criminal Justice Information:

NATIONAL CRIMINAL JUSTICE REFERENCE SERVICE
P.O. Box 6000
Rockville, MD 20849-6000
(800)851-3420
www.ncjrs.org

The NCJRS provides a broad range of national and international criminal and juvenile justice information. NCJRS serves as the information clearinghouse for several governmental organizations. By logging onto the NCJRS site, information from the various agencies is available:

> U.S. Department of Justice
> Bureau of Justice Statistics
> National Institute of Justice
> Bureau of Justice Assistance
> Office for Victims of Crime
> Office of Juvenile Justice & Delinquency
> Prevention (this office publishes the Juvenile
> Justice Journal which is also available through
> the NCJRS site at www.ncjrs.org/ojjdp/jjjournal)

BUREAU OF JUVENILE STATISTICS
www.ojp.usdoj.gov.bjs

This site contains statistics about crimes and victims, drugs and crime, homicide trends, criminal offenders, the justice system, law enforcement, prosecution, courts and sentencing, corrections, and crime and justice data from other sources

AMERICAN BAR ASSOCIATION-Juvenile Justice Center
750 N. Lake Shore Drive
Chicago, IL 60611   (312)988-5000
www.abanet.org/crimjust/juvjus/home

The ABA site offers information about legislation
on juvenile issues on both the state and federal level.
You can also find changes in laws that impact
juveniles.

JUVENILE INFO NETWORK
www.juvenilenet.org

This is a site dedicated to correctional professionals
involved with juvenile corrections.

INSTITUTE FOR INTERGOVERNMENTAL RESEARCH
www.iir.com

Specializes in information and articles on law
enforcement, juvenile justice, criminal justice and
justice data from other sites.

JUVENILE JUSTICE CLEARINGHOUSE—Florida State
University and Florida A&M University
www.fsu.edu/~crimdo/jjclearinghouse

Has great links to the juvenile and criminal justice
system (also try www.criminology.fsu.edu/cj).

AMNESTY INTERNATIONAL
www.amnesty.org

Articles on the state of adult and juvenile justice
systems.

U.S. FEDERAL GOVERNMENT AGENCIES DIRECTORY
www.lib.lsu.edu/gov/fedgov.html

Delinquency Prevention & School Resources:

KEEP SCHOOLS SAFE (NAAG & NASB)
www.keepschoolssafe.org

CENTERS FOR DISEASE CONTROL & PREVENTION
Division of Violence Prevention
www.cdc.gov/ncipc
(On the homepage, click on "Violence Prevention" for
available articles.)

U.S. DEPARTMENT OF EDUCATION
400 Maryland Ave. S.W.
Washington, D.C. 20202-0498
(800) USA-Learn
Early Warning, Timely Response: A Guide to Safe Schools
www.ed.gov
(On the homepage, click on "Safe Schools".)

ONE TO ONE, THE NATIONAL MENTORING
PARTNERSHIP
www.mentoring.org/

Substance Abuse:

NATIONAL CENTER ON ADDICTION AND SUBSTANCE
ABUSE AT COLUMBIA UNIVERSITY
www.casacolumbia.org

THE OFFICE OF NATIONAL DRUG CONTROL POLICY
www.whitehousedrugpolicy.gov

NATIONAL CLEARINGHOUSE OF ALCOHOL AND DRUG
INFORMATION
www.health.org

Juvenile Statistics:

CHILD TRENDS
www.childtrends.org

CENTERS FOR DISEASE CONTROL AND PREVENTION
Youth Risk Behavior National Survey
www.cdc.gov
(On the homepage, search for "Youth Risk Behavior".)

SUBSTANCE ABUSE AND MENTAL HEALTH SERVICES
ADMINISTRATION, U.S. DEPARTMENT OF HEALTH
AND HUMAN SERVICES
www.samhsa.gov

Law Enforcement Site:

COPNET AND POLICE RESOURCE LIST
www.police.sas.ab.ca
Link to law enforcement sites

Gang Information Site:

US DEPARTMENT OF JUSTICE
950 Pennsylvania Ave. N.W.
Washington, D.C. 20530-001
www.usdoc.gov/ag/anti-gang.htm

Forensic Science Site:

BUREAU OF FORENSIC SERVICES
www.caag.state.ca.us/bfs/index

Collect, analyze and compare physical evidence from
crime scenes and persons

Games:

EVIDENCE - THE TRUE WITNESS
http://library.advanced.org/17049

This award winning site allows the player to become a detective and solve a crime through the use of forensic evidence (DNA, fingerprints, etc.). The site also includes information about general information on forensic science, careers in forensic science and links to other forensic sites.

INTERACTIVE DETECTIVE STORIES
www.geocities.com/Area51/Cavern/2016/interactive.

COURT TV
www.courttv.com/games

Legal Pursuit is a series of multiple choice questions about the law.

State Bar Associations:

State Bar Associations:

ALABAMA STATE BAR
415 Dexter Avenue
Montgomery, AL 36104
phone (334) 269-1515 fax (334) 261-6310
www.alabar.org

ALASKA BAR ASSOCIATION
510 L Street, Suite 602
Anchorage, AK 99501
phone (907) 272-7469   fax (907) 272-2932
www.alaskabar.org

ARKANSAS BAR ASSOCIATION
400 West Markham
Little Rock, AR 72201
phone (501) 375-4606   fax (501) 375-4901
www.arkbar.com

STATE BAR OF ARIZONA
111 West Monroe
Suite 1800 Phoenix, AZ 85003-1742
phone (602) 252-4804   fax (602) 271-4930
www.azbar.org

STATE BAR OF CALIFORNIA
555 Franklin Street
San Francisco, CA 94102
phone (415) 561-8200

1149 South Hill Street
915 L Street, Suite 1260
Los Angeles, CA 90015-2299
Sacramento, CA 95814-3705
phone (213) 765-1000   fax (213) 765-1029
URL: "http://www.calbar.org"http://www.calbar.org

COLORADO BAR ASSOCIATION
1900 Grant Street, 9th Floor
Denver, CO 80203
phone (303) 860-1115   fax (303) 894-0821

CONNECTICUT BAR ASSOCIATION
101 Corporate Place
Rocky Hill, CT 06067-1894
phone (860) 721-0025   fax (860) 257-4125

DELAWARE STATE BAR ASSOCIATION
1201 Orange Street
Suite 1100
Wilmington, DE 19801
phone (302) 658-5279   fax (302) 658-5212

THE DISTRICT OF COLUMBIA BAR
1250 H Street, N.W.
Washington, D.C. 20005-5937
phone (202) 737-4700   fax (202) 626-3471
www.dcbar.org

THE FLORIDA BAR
650 Apalachee Parkway
Tallahassee, FL 32399-2300
phone (850) 561-5600   fax (850) 561-5827
www.flabar.org

STATE BAR OF GEORGIA
800 The Hurt Building
50 Hurt Plaza
Atlanta, GA 30303
phone (404) 527-8700   fax (404) 527-8717

HAWAII STATE BAR ASSOCIATION
1136 Union Mall
Penthouse 1
Honolulu, HI 96813
phone (808) 537-1868   fax (808) 521-7936

IDAHO STATE BAR
525 West Jefferson Street
Boise, ID 83701
phone (208) 334-4500   fax (208) 334-4515

ILLINOIS STATE BAR ASSOCIATION
Bar Center (Headquarters)
424 S. Second St.
Springfield, IL 62701-1779
(800) 252-8908 (toll-free in Illinois)
(217) 525-1760 phone   (217) 525-0712 fax
www.illinoisbar.org

IOWA STATE BAR ASSOCIATION
521 East Locus
3rd Floor
Des Moines, Iowa 50309
(515)243-3179 phone   (515)243-2511 fax
www.iowabar.org

INDIANA STATE BAR ASSOCIATION
Indiana Bar Center
230 East Ohio Street
Indianapolis, IN 46204-2199
(317) 639-5465 phone   (317) 266-2588 fax
www.iquest.net/isba/

KANSAS BAR ASSOCIATION
1200 SW Harrison
P.O. Box 1037
Topeka, KS 66601-1037
(785) 234-5696 phone   (785) 234-3813 fax

KENTUCKY BAR ASSOCIATION
514 West Main Street
Frankfort, KY 40601-1883
(502) 564-3795 phone   (502) 564-3225 fax

LOUISIANA STATE BAR ASSOCIATION
601 St. Charles Avenue
New Orleans, LA 70130-3427
(504) 566-1600 phone   (504) 566-0930 fax

MASSACHUSETTS BAR ASSOCIATION
20 West Street
Boston, MA 02111
(617) 338-0500 phone   (617) 338-0650 fax

MARYLAND STATE BAR ASSOCIATION, INC
The Maryland Bar Center
520 West Fayette Street
Baltimore, MD 21201
(410) 685-7878 phone   (410) 837-0518 fax
www.msba.org

MAINE STATE BAR ASSOCIATION
P.O. Box 788
Augusta, ME 04332-0788
(207) 622-7523 phone   (207) 623-0083 fax
www.mainebar.org

STATE BAR OF MICHIGAN
Michael Franck Building
306 Townsend Street
Lansing, MI 48933-2083
(800) 968-1442 phone   (517) 482-6248 fax

MINNESOTA STATE BAR ASSOCIATION
600 Nicollet Mall, Suite 380
Minneapolis, MN 55402
(612) 333-1183 phone   (612) 333-4927 fax

THE MISSOURI BAR
The Missouri Bar Center
326 Monroe St.
Jefferson City, MO 65102-0119
(573) 635-4128 phone   (573) 635-2811 fax
www.mobar.org

THE MISSISSIPPI BAR
643 North State Street
Jackson, MS 39202
www.msbar.org

STATE BAR OF MONTANA
46 N. Last Chance Gulch, #2A
Helena, MT 59601
(406) 442-7660 phone   (406) 442-7763 fax
Lawyer Referral Service (406) 449-6577

NORTH CAROLINA STATE BAR
208 Fayetteville Street Mall
Raleigh, North Carolina 27601
(919) 828-4620 phone   (919) 821-9168 fax

THE STATE BAR ASSOCIATION OF NORTH DAKOTA
Suite 101
515 1/2 East Broadway
P.O. Box 2136
Bismarck, ND 58502
(701) 255-1404 phone   (701) 224-1621 fax

NEBRASKA STATE BAR ASSOCIATION
Roman L. Hruska Law Center
635 South 14th Street
Lincoln, NE 68508
(402)475-7091 phone   (402) 475-7089 fax

NEW HAMPSHIRE BAR ASSOCIATION
112 Pleasant Street
Concord, NH 03301-2947
(603)224-6942 phone (603)224-2910 fax
(603)229-0002 (Lawyer Referral Service)

NEW JERSEY STATE BAR ASSOCIATION
New Jersey Law Center
One Constitution Square
New Brunswick, NJ 08901-1500
(732)937-7500 phone   (732) 224-2910 fax

STATE BAR OF NEW MEXICO
5121 Masthead NE
Albuquerque, NM 87109
(505) 797-6000 phone   (505) 843-8765 fax

NEW YORK STATE BAR ASSOCIATION
One Elk Street
Albany, NY 12207
(518) 463-3200 phone   (518) 463-8527 fax
www.nysba.org

OHIO STATE BAR ASSOCIATION
1700 Lake Shore Drive
Columbus, OH 43216
(614) 487-2050 phone   (614) 487-1008 fax
Office of Government Affairs
88 East Broad St., Ste 870
Columbus, OH 43215
(614) 221-6983 phone   (614) 221-5072 fax

OKLAHOMA BAR ASSOCIATION
1901 N. Lincoln
Oklahoma City, OK 73105
(405) 524-2365 phone   (405) 416-7001 fax

OREGON STATE BAR
5200 S.W. Meadows Road
Lake Oswego, OR 97035
(503) 620-0222 phone   toll free (800) 452-8260
(503) 684-1366 fax
www.osbar.org

PENNSYLVANIA BAR ASSOCIATION
100 South Street
Harrisburg, PA 17101
(800) 932-0311 phone   (717) 238-7182 fax

RHODE ISLAND BAR ASSOCIATION
115 Cedar Street
Providence, RI 02903
(401) 421-5740 phone   (401) 421-2703 fax

SOUTH CAROLINA BAR
950 Taylor Street
Columbia, SC 29201
(803) 799-6653 phone   (803) 799-4118 fax

THE STATE BAR OF SOUTH DAKOTA
222 East Capitol
Pierre, SD 57501
(605) 224-7554 phone   (605) 224-0282 fax
www.sdbar.org

TENNESSEE BAR ASSOCIATION
3622 West End Avenue
Nashville, TN 37205-2403
(615) 383-7421 phone (615) 297-8058 fax

STATE BAR OF TEXAS
Mailing Address
P.O. Box 12487
Austin, TX 78711
(800) 204-2222 phone (512) 463-1463 phone
(512) 463-1475 fax

UTAH STATE BAR
645 South 200 East
Salt Lake City, UT 84111
(801) 531-9077 phone (801) 531-0660 fax
www.utahbar.org

VIRGINIA STATE BAR
Eighth and Main Building
707 East Main Street, Suite 1500
Richmond, VA 23219
(804) 775-0500 phone (804) 775-0501 fax
www.vsb.org

VERMONT BAR ASSOCIATION
35-37 Court Street
Montpelier, VT 05602
(802) 223-2020 phone (800) 639-7036 phone
(802) 223-1573 fax
www.vtbar.org

WASHINGTON STATE BAR ASSOCIATION
2101 Fourth Avenue, 4th Floor
Seattle, WA 98121-2330
(206) 727-8200 phone
(206) 727-8320 fax

STATE BAR OF WISCONSIN
402 W. Wilson Street
Madison WI 53703
(608) 257-3838 phone   (608) 257-5502 fax

THE WEST VIRGINIA STATE BAR
2006 Kanawha Boulevard, East
Charleston, WV 25311
(304) 558-2456 phone   (304) 558-2467 fax
www.wvbar.org

WYOMING STATE BAR
500 Randall Avenue
Cheyenne, WY 82001
(307) 632-9061 phone   (307) 632-3737 fax

GLOSSARY

ACCIDENT RE-CONSTRUCTION — When an expert evaluates the scene of an accident to determine the cause, speed of the vehicles and fault of the parties.

ARRAIGNMENT — Usually the first court appearance. When an accused person comes before the court and enters a plea to the criminal charge or charges made against him.

ARREST WARRANT — A written order issued by a Judge that authorizes the arrest of a person.

ASSAULT — Attempted battery and causing fear of immediate battery. For example, throwing a punch at someone, but it misses, or making a gesture that causes someone to think you're going to hurt them. See battery.

ATTEMPT — A significant, but unsuccessful effort to commit a crime. An act that falls short of completing the crime.

ATTORNEY — A person who has completed law school, passed the state bar exam and is licensed by the state to practice law. Also know as a lawyer or counsel.

AUTO BURGLARY — Breaking into a vehicle with the intent to commit a crime, usually to steal something in the vehicle.

AUTO THEFT — Stealing a vehicle. If a vehicle is stolen from the driver by use of force or fear, the crime becomes a robbery or carjacking.

BAIL — Collateral usually in the form of money or property that is used as a guarantee to make sure a person who is charged with a crime appears for his court appearances. If the person is able to post the bail with the court or through a bail bondsman, he will be released from custody. If a person is not able to post the allotted bail, he will remain in custody. A minor who is charged in juvenile court is not entitled to bail. A juvenile will either be released to the custody of a parent or guardian or kept in custody.

BAIL BOND — A bail bond is similar to an insurance policy. The bonds person posts the bond and the defendant will then be released from custody on bail.

BAIL BONDS PERSON — Individuals licensed to write bonds.

BAILIFF — A court officer, usually a marshall or sheriff, who insures the safety and order in the courtroom. The Bailiff handles prisoners and is responsible for the jury during a trial. Also known as a Marshall.

BATTERY — Causing bodily injury to another person.

BEYOND A REASONABLE DOUBT — What a reasonable person would believe. In a criminal trial, a juror must be convinced beyond a reasonable doubt that the defendant is guilty of violating the law.

BLOOD ALCOHOL LEVEL — The amount of alcohol in the blood. If you are suspected of driving under the influence, you are obligated by law to take a test administered by the police that measures the alcohol in your blood. The measurement can be done by 1). a breathalyzer: you breathe into a machine which measures your alcohol level through your breath; 2). urine test: you give a urine sample which is tested for your alcohol level; or 3). blood test: a sample of your blood is taken and tested to determine your blood alcohol level. In most states, if you refuse to take the test, you are assumed to be guilty.

BOOKED INTO CUSTODY— When a suspect is arrested, he is transported to the police station where his fingerprints and mug shot are taken. The charges against him are determined and the bail amount is set. Also known as Booking.

BOOT CAMP — A form of punishment for juvenile offenders. Includes a strict, regimented program of discipline, responsibility, exercise, hard work and school. Programs are usually designed after the military boot camps. Boot camp is not available in all states.

BURGLARY — When a person enters a building with the intent to commit a theft. Can be residential or commercial: **Residential**: Burglary of a place where people live. A residential burglary is considered more serious than a commercial burglary. That's because people live in residences and the risk of injuring them during a burglary is thought to be greater. **Commercial**: Burglary of a business, warehouse or any type of commercial building, including new construction.

CARJACKING — Stealing a vehicle from the driver by using force or fear.

CIVIL CASE — Legal action that involves suing another person for money or equity (return of property).

CITY ATTORNEY — An attorney for the city, with the duty of prosecuting people who have been accused of a crime. The City Attorney's Office usually handles misdemeanor cases.

CO-DEFENDANT — When two or more people are charged together in the same criminal case, each is called a co-defendant. Each co-defendant is entitled to his or her own attorney.

CO-CONSPIRATOR — A person who plans with others to commit a crime.

COMMUNITY SERVICE — A condition of probation available in most adult and juvenile courts. The defendant is required to complete a specified number of hours working at a court-approved job in the community, such as trash pick-up and graffiti removal.

COMPUTER FRAUD — Changing or distorting information in a computer system without permission. The information that is changed must be something that others rely on.

CONCURRENT SENTENCING — Multiple terms of imprisonment that run at the same time. For instance, John receives a sixteen month sentence for Possession of a Controlled Substance and a twenty-four month sentence for Forgery. If the sentences run concurrent, the most time he would serve is twenty-four months.

CONSECUTIVE SENTENCING — Multiple terms of imprisonment that run one after the other and are served individually. For instance, John receives a sixteen month sentence for Possession of a Controlled Substance and a twenty-four month sentence for Forgery. If the sentences run consecutively, John would serve the sixteen month sentence and the twenty four months sentence separately for a total of forty months.

CONSPIRACY — An agreement between two or more people to commit an illegal act. Talking about committing a crime is not sufficient. Overt action must be taken for there to be a conspiracy.

CONSTITUTION — The Constitution of the United States is the ultimate law of our land. Each state also has a Constitution.

CONSTITUTIONAL RIGHTS — The U.S. Constitution guarantees our rights and is the foundation of our laws.

CONTROLLED SUBSTANCE — Substances that are regulated by the state. Possession of such substances or their components without permission is a criminal offense.

CONVICTION — When a Judge or jury finds a defendant guilty of a crime. If a defendant enters into a plea agreement and pleads guilty to a violation of a criminal law, that is also a conviction. After a defendant is convicted he is sentenced.

COUNTY JAIL — A county run facility where people who are in custody are held. If a person has been charged with a crime and has not posted bail or bail has not been granted, he is usually detained in a county jail. If a defendant is awaiting trial, he will be detained in a county jail. If a defendant has been convicted of certain crimes, he may be sentenced to serve time in a county jail.

COURT TRIAL — see Judge Trial

CRIMINAL CHARGE — When the District Attorney's office believes a person has committed a crime and there is sufficient evidence to prove the crime, the D.A. will file a formal, written Criminal Complaint against the person. The Complaint will list the crime the person is suspected of violating. The criminal offense is referred to as a charge against the defendant.

CRIMINAL STATUTE SECTION — Laws are referred to as statutes or codes. Each statute represents an individual law and is assigned a different number. This number is the section number.

CRIMINAL CONSPIRACY — When two or more people act together to commit a crime.

CRIMINAL COURT — The division of the court system that handles prosecution of criminal laws.

DEATH PENALTY — Being put to death for the crime or crimes you have committed. First degree murder and certain other offenses carry as punishment a penalty of death. In those states that do not have the death penalty, the maximum punishment is life in prison without parole (LWOP)

DEFENSE — When a defendant introduces evidence in his or her trial to refute the prosecution's theory of guilt.

DEFENSE ATTORNEY— The lawyer who represents the defendant in court.

DELINQUENCY COURT — The court where criminal cases involving juveniles are handled.

DEPENDENCY COURT — The court that oversees juveniles who have been removed from their homes due to neglect, abuse or when the parents cannot deal with the child's problems.

DISCHARGING A WEAPON INTO AN INHABITED DWELLING — Firing a weapon into a house or building where people live or work. Considered a serious crime.

DISTRICT ATTORNEY (D.A.) — A lawyer employed by the county, with the duty of prosecuting people accused of crimes. The District Attorney's office handles misdemeanor and felony cases. Also known as a prosecutor.

DRIVING UNDER THE INFLUENCE OF ALCOHOL OR DRUGS — Driving a vehicle when your blood alcohol level is over the legal limit. Also known as Driving While Intoxicated or Drunk Driving.

DUMPING OF TOXIC WASTE — Illegally dumping waste or material that may be hazardous or toxic.

DRUG REHABILITATION — A program where people with drug abuse problems receive help with their addiction.

DRUG TESTING — A test to determine if your system contains controlled substances. Urine tests are the most common way to test for drugs in a person's system. Drug testing may also be a condition of probation. Testing positive for illegal drugs is a probation violation.

ELECTRONIC MONITORING — As part of probation, a minor or adult can be placed on electronic monitoring. An electronic device (ankle bracelet) is attached to the ankle. If the person wearing the monitor attempts to leave home, the monitoring station is alerted. Failure to comply with electronic monitoring is a violation of probation.

ELEMENTS OF A CRIME — Each part of a crime is referred to as an element. Each element of the crime must be proven beyond a reasonable doubt in a criminal trial for a defendant to be found guilty.

Example: **Residential Burglary**

      1st element: Entry into a residence

      2nd element: Without permission

      3rd element: With the intent to commit a crime.

The prosecution must first prove that the defendant entered into someone's residence, that he or she entered without the owner's permission and that the defendant entered with the intent to commit a crime.

FAMILY LAW COURT — Where issues such as divorce, child custody and spousal support are decided.

FELONY — A capital crime punishable by imprisonment in state prison or by death.

FIFTH AMENDMENT — The 5th Amendment of the Constitution guarantees the right against self-incrimination. It also guarantees you cannot be tried twice for the same crime (known as double jeopardy).

FIELD SOBRIETY TESTS — A series of tests given by police to suspects believed to be under the influence of alcohol or illegal drugs. The tests measure physical coordination and the ability to follow simple verbal instructions. The police will administer the tests and use the results to reach an opinion as to whether a suspect is under the influence. If the tests indicate intoxication, the suspect will be required to submit to a blood, urine or breathalyzer test to confirm or deny the officer's opinion.

FILING OF A CRIMINAL COMPLAINT — When the District Attorney's office reviews the police report and decides to file a criminal complaint against the suspect in the criminal court.

FINGER PRINTING — The process of taking an inked impression of someone's finger pads. Used in forensic science for the purpose of identification.

FISH — Slang term used to describe a new inmate.

FORENSIC SCIENCE — A process where evidence from crime scenes is analyzed, including blood, fingerprints, suspect profiles, DNA.

FORFEITURE — When the police seize a suspect's property or possessions, believing they were acquired through illegal means. The District Attorney's office will begin forfeiture proceedings in an attempt to permanently deprive a suspect of his property.

FOURTH AMENDMENT — The 4th Amendment of the United States Constitution guarantees the right against unreasonable search and seizure of your home and property. To search your home or property, law enforcement must obtain a warrant. There are exceptions to the warrant requirement. Some exceptions are: if you are on probation or parole, if it's an emergency situation or if the police are in hot pursuit of someone.

FOSTER HOME — A home for children who are wards of the court.

FRAUD — When someone intentionally misrepresents or lies about facts which other people rely on.

FRESH MEAT — Slang term used to refer to new inmates.

GRAFFITI — Writing on the property of others for destructive purposes.

GRAFFITI REMOVAL — A sentencing option available in some juvenile courts. Similar to community service. As a condition of probation, a minor will be ordered by the Judge to complete a set number of hours of graffiti removal.

GRAND THEFT — see Theft.

GUILTY — When a Judge or jury finds a defendant has committed a crime, or the defendant declares his or her guilt as part of a plea agreement.

HABITUAL OFFENDER — A repeat offender. The law increases the penalties for repeat offenders.

HARD LABOR — Strenuous, physical labor. As part of probation, a defendant can be ordered by the court to complete a specified number of hours of hard labor .

HOME ON PROBATION — A sentencing option available in some juvenile courts. A minor is allowed to go home as a condition of probation, but must still follow the terms and conditions set by the court.

HUNG JURY — When a jury is unable to reach a verdict.

ILLEGAL NARCOTICS — see Controlled Substance.

INDIGENT DEFENDANT — A person charged with a crime who cannot afford an attorney. If a defendant in a criminal proceeding cannot afford to hire an attorney, the court will appoint an attorney to represent him or her.

INFORMATION — A formal, written document charging a defendant with a crime. The Information is prepared by the prosecution and filed with the court. Also known as a Complaint.

JAIL — Usually a county run facility where defendants are housed while awaiting trial or serving their sentence.

JUDGE — A person who is appointed by the governor or elected by the voters of the state to preside over a courtroom. The Judge will hear cases, decide disputes and settle controversies between the parties to a case. If the Judge presides over criminal cases, he or she will sentence defendants who are found guilty. Also known as Commissioner, Magistrate.

JUDGE TRIAL — A trial held before a Judge without a jury. A defendant may waive his right to a jury trial and agree to have the trial heard by the Judge. The Judge hears the evidence and then decides if the defendant is guilty or not guilty. Also known as a court trial or a bench trial.

JUROR — A person chosen to sit on a jury.

JURY — A specified number of people (in a criminal trial, usually twelve) who are selected by the prosecution and defense counsel to decide whether a defendant is guilty or not guilty. Most states do not allow for juries in juvenile delinquency trials.

JURY DELIBERATION — When the jury retires to the jury room to discuss the facts of the case to determine if the defendant is guilty or not guilty.

JUVENILE — Person under the age of eighteen (can vary from state to state).

JUVENILE COURT — A court specifically designated to handle juvenile delinquency cases. The philosophy of most juvenile courts is to rehabilitate delinquent minors as well as to protect the community. In some states, the juvenile court is part of the family court system.

JUVENILE HALL / JUVENILE DETENTION CENTER — A facility set up to house minors involved in the juvenile delinquency system. Minors awaiting trial may be housed in a juvenile detention center. Minors may also be sentenced to time in a juvenile delinquency center.

KIDNAPPING — Taking of a person against their will.

LAW — A rule passed by the legislature designed to guide people's behavior. Also known as a statute.

LIFE IN PRISON WITHOUT PAROLE — **(LWOP)** A sentence where the defendant spends the rest of his or her life in prison without any possibility of parole.

MALICE — Action that shows an extreme indifference to human life, infliction of great bodily harm or intent to kill.

MANDATORY SENTENCE — By law, convictions on certain crimes require a mandatory sentence. The Judge has no discretion and must impose the mandatory sentence.

MANSLAUGHTER — The unlawful killing of a human being without malice.

MANUFACTURING OF ILLEGAL NARCOTICS — Making a controlled substance.

MARIJUANA — A leafy plant also known as Cannabis. The plant is dried, then smoked. Marijuana is used for its narcotic effect. Marijuana is a controlled substance and its use and cultivation is illegal. Also known as weed, pot and by many other names.

METHAMPHETAMINE — A powdery or rock substance which is inhaled into the nasal passages, smoked or injected. Methamphetamine is used for its narcotic effect and is highly addictive. Since it is a controlled substance, use, possession, transportation, sale and manufacture of Methamphetamine is illegal. Also known as speed, crank, or meth.

MINOR — Person under the age of eighteen. See Juvenile.

MIRANDA RIGHTS — When a suspect is in custody <u>and</u> is being interrogated by law enforcement, he or she must be read the Miranda Rights. Miranda rights are:

1. The right to remain silent. "You have the right to remain silent. Anything you say can and will be used against you in a court of law."

2. The right to an attorney. "You have the right to an attorney. If you cannot afford an attorney, the court will appoint one for you."

MIRANDA WARNINGS — When a defendant is in police custody <u>and</u> is being questioned, the police must notify the defendant of the right to remain silent and the right to have an attorney present at any questioning.

MISDEMEANOR — Criminal violation of the law that is less serious than a felony. The penalty for a misdemeanor can range from no time in jail up to a maximum of one year in a county jail. A misdemeanor is not punishable by imprisonment in state prison.

MISTRIAL— A Judge can declare a mistrial if the jury is deadlocked and cannot reach a verdict or when an error occurs during the trial proceedings that cannot be corrected.

MURDER — An unlawful killing of a human being with malice. There are two degrees of murder:

1st degree murder: Any murder committed with premeditation and deliberation.

2nd degree murder: Includes all other types of murder.

NEGLIGENCE — Failure to act as a reasonable person under the circumstances.

NO CONTEST (NO LO CONTENDERE) — Plea entered by a defendant to a criminal charge. No contest means the defendant will not contest the sentence of the court, but is not admitting guilt. The court views a "no contest" plea the same as a guilty plea. People sometimes enter into a no contest plea to avoid admitting guilt, or if they are concerned about being sued in a civil court.

NOT GUILTY — A plea entered by a defendant to a criminal charge. Not guilty is a denial of the criminal charges.

PAROLE — After a person is released from prison, he is required to abide by certain terms and conditions for a period of time. This is known as parole. Parole is managed by the state prison system. If a person violates parole, he or she can be sent back to prison. A person on parole is referred to as a parolee.

PAROLE OFFICER — Each person released from state prison is assigned to a Parole Officer. The Parole Officer monitors a person's progress after his or her release. Parole Officers have the authority to violate a person's parole and send him back to prison.

PAROLE BOARD — A group of individuals selected to review and evaluate the parole status of prisoners who are eligible for parole. The parole board determines if the person should be released from prison. Members of the parole board also evaluate parolees who have been charged with violating parole. They determine if the parolee should go back to prison for their violation and for how long.

PENITENTIARY — A state or federal prison.

PLACEMENT — In juvenile court, a minor who is found to have violated a criminal law is declared a ward of the court. The court may place the minor in a foster home or youth facility.

PLEA — A defendant's answer to the criminal charges that have been filed against him. A defendant can enter a plea of "guilty", "not guilty" or "no contest".

PLEA AGREEMENT/PLEA BARGAIN — The negotiation process where the prosecutor and the defense attorney reach an agreement as to the disposition of the case. The defendant must agree to the plea bargain, and it must be approved by the Judge.

POLICE REPORT — A report prepared by officers involved in a criminal investigation.

POSSESSION OF ALCOHOL IN A VEHICLE — A minor cannot have alcohol in a vehicle whether the container is open or closed. An adult can have an open container in most types of vehicle as long as it is properly stored, usually in the trunk.

POSSESSION OF AN OPEN CONTAINER IN A VEHICLE — Having an open container of any alcoholic beverage inside the passenger compartment of a vehicle is against the law.

POSSESSION OF A CONTROLLED SUBSTANCE — Having a controlled substance illegally in your possession.

POSSESSION FOR SALE OF A CONTROLLED SUBSTANCE — Attempting to sell or selling a controlled substance illegally in your possession.

PRESUMPTION OF INNOCENCE — In a criminal trial, a defendant is considered innocent until proven guilty beyond a reasonable doubt. Until the prosecution proves the defendant's guilt, he or she is presumed innocent of the charges.

PRISON — A correctional facility run by the state, set up for the imprisonment of criminals who have committed serious offenses.

PRISON FOR JUVENILE OFFENDERS — A correctional facility set up for imprisonment of juvenile offenders who have committed seriousor violent crimes.

PROBATION — If a defendant is found guilty of a misdemeanor, the Judge may place the person on a county supervised program known as probation. The terms and conditions of probation may include doing time in the county jail. Under certain conditions, a defendant found guilty of a felony may be placed on probation by the Judge, rather than being sent to prison.

PROBATION VIOLATION — A defendant who is on probation and fails to meet all of the terms and conditions may be sent back to court for violating probation. If it is a minor violation, the Judge may order the probationer to continue probation under the same terms and conditions. If the violation is more severe, the Judge may impose a harsher sentence, including time in custody.

PROSECUTOR— Lawyers from the District Attorney's and City Attorney's office who file the Complaints and try the cases against defendants.

PUBLIC DEFENDER — An attorney who represents people who cannot afford to hire a private attorney. A public defender is employed by the city or county to defend indigent defendants.

PUNISHMENT — Any penalty imposed on a person by the legal system. The penalty may be a fine, imprisonment, denial or loss of personal rights or privileges, deportation or death.

RAPE — Sexual assault of a person without their consent.

RECKLESS DRIVING UNDER THE INFLUENCE OF ALCOHOL OR DRUGS & CAUSING INJURY — Causing an injury to another person while driving under the influence of alcohol or drugs.

RESIDENTIAL LIVE-IN FACILITY FOR JUVENILES — If a juvenile is declared a ward of the court and the Judge determines that he or she cannot return home, one of the Judge's options is to place the juvenile in a county facility — either a group home, foster home, or other controlled living arrangement.

RESTITUTION — Reimbursement, repayment, or compensation for loss, damage or injury to a victim.

ROBBERY — Stealing from a person with the use of force or fear.

SEARCH WARRANT — A written order issued and signed by a Judge which allows law enforcement to search a location for specified items.

SELF-INCRIMINATION — The 5th Amendment prohibits the use of coerced confessions. You cannot be forced or intimidated by law enforcement to make damaging statements against yourself.

SENTENCE — The punishment ordered by a court after a finding or admission of guilt.

SERIOUS & VIOLENT OFFENDER LAW — Also known as the 'strike' law. A law requiring mandatory long-term sentencing for certain crimes committed by habitual offenders.

SHOPKEEPER'S PRIVILEGE — A law which allows employees of a store to search and detain people whom they believe have committed a theft within their store.

SIXTH AMENDMENT — Guarantees the right to be represented by an attorney to anyone arrested or charged with a criminal violation.

STATE PRISON — A place where convicted felons are confined for the duration of their sentence.

STATE PENITENTIARY — see State Prison.

STATUTE — A law enacted by the legislature.

STATUTE OF LIMITATION —A law which sets a time restriction for filing a legal action. There is no statute of limitation on murder.

STAY — When a sentence is suspended by an order of the court. The stay can be temporary or permanent.

STRIKE — A criminal charge or conviction considered by statute to be serious or violent. A strike can be used to increase sentencing in future crimes.

SUBPOENA — An order from the court which requires a person to appear in court to testify.

THEFT — The taking of another's personal property with the intent to permanently deprive them of their property. **Petty Theft**: If the value of the stolen property is small, the crime will be considered a petty theft. **Grand Theft**: If the value of the stolen property has a higher dollar amount, the crime will be considered grand theft. Theft is also known as larceny.

THIRD STRIKE OFFENSE — In some states, a law which requires a defendant who is found guilty of a third felony to be sentenced to a mandatory prison term of twenty-five years to life.

THROWING OBJECTS AT A VEHICLE — It is a crime to intentionally throw objects at a vehicle with the purpose of frightening or injuring the occupant.

TRESPASS — Intentionally going on the property of another without permission.

TRIAL — A legal proceeding to determine if a defendant is guilty or not guilty of a crime.

TRIAL COURT — Court of law where a trial is held.

VANDALISM — Intentional destruction of property belonging to another.

VERDICT — The decision of the jury.

VEHICULAR MANSLAUGHTER — The unlawful killing of a human being with a vehicle. See Manslaughter.

WARD OF THE COURT — A child who has been taken from the custody of the parent or guardian. Custody of the child is transferred to the county.

INDEX

A

adult, trial as. *See* juvenile vs. adult court
age. *See* juvenile vs. adult court
alcohol. *See also* drinking and driving
  alcohol level and tests, 7, 10-11
  drinking, legal age for, 6, 10-12
  early drinking leading to addiction (statistics), 138
  field sobriety tests, 3-5, 11-12
  substance abuse, list of resources, 169-170
  teenage drinkers (statistics), 138
Amnesty International, 168
appeals on death sentence, 153-154
arraignment, 83, 148
Assault with a Deadly Weapon, 20, 24

B

bail, 87, 103
Bar Associations
  American Bar Association, 168
  State Bar Associations, 172-180
blood test (alcohol), 7, 10-12
boot camp, 21, 26
  escape from, 126
  lifestyle at, 99
breathalyzer (alcohol), 7, 10-12
Burglary, 27-48, 105-118

C

Carjacking, 115, 126
cheating, college entrance exams, 75-88
community service/hard labor, 26
Computer Fraud, 75-88
computer games, 171
Conspiracy, Criminal, 75-88

Note: The names of laws are capitalized in this index.
For definitions, please consult the glossary of this book.

counseling, 99-100
county jail, 137
Criminal Conspiracy, 75-88
criminal statutes. *See* laws
curfew, 25
custody, 103
     minor's release to parents, 35, 97, 103

D
death sentence, 153-154
     minimum age for death penalty, 158
     minors and the death sentence, 156
     number now on death row (crimes committed as
          juveniles), 158
Defacement of Property, 27-48
delinquency prevention, 169
District Attorney's office, 72-73
drinking. *See* alcohol
drinking and driving, 1-12, 129-138. *See also* alcohol
     Driving Under the Influence (D.U.I.) of
          Alcohol or Drugs, 1-12
     penalties for D.U.I and possession, 8-12
     Possession of Alcohol in a Vehicle by
          Persons under 21 Years, 1-12
     Reckless D.U.I. and Causing Bodily Injury, 129-138
driving fatalities (statistics), 71-73. *See also* drinking and
driving
driving under the influence. *See* drinking and driving
drugs
     drug dealing, 89, 103, 139-158
     Habitual Offender, 105-118
     hard drugs, 139
     manufacture or sale of 1/2 ounce, 126
     "meth" (methamphetamine), 94, 112
     Possession for Sale of a Controlled Substance, 89-103, 112
     Providing a Room for Storage and/or Distribution of
          a Controlled Substance, 89-103
     selling to a minor, 115
     substance abuse, list of resources, 169-170
D.U.I. *See* alcohol; drinking and driving

E

educational resources, 169
electronic monitoring, 85, 88
Environmental Protection Agency, 163

F

felonies, 45, 71-73
       judge's choice of prison or jail, 137
       list of serious and violent offenses, 115
       statute of limitation, 165
       subsequent felony convictions, 115
       Third Felony Conviction, 105-118
       "third strike law" (felonies), 116
       use of deadly weapon during felony, 115
firearms. *See* weapons
force, use of, 55
forensic science site, 170
foster home (or facility) placement, 26

G

games, 171
gangs, 89-103, 119-127
       gang information site, 170
government, 167-170
       Institute for Intergovernmental Research, 168
       National Criminal Justice Reference Service
(various agencies), 167
       U.S. Federal Government Agencies Directory, 168
Grand Theft, 49-64
guns. *See* weapons

H

Habitual Offender, 105-118
hacking, 75-88
hiring someone to commit a crime, 75-88. *See also*
       Conspiracy, Criminal

J

jails, 137
juries

alternate jurors, 157
hung jury, 157
jury's role in murder trial, 156
juvenile justice, organizations and resources, 167-171
    Juvenile Info Network, 168
    Juvenile Justice Center, American Bar
    Association, 168
    Juvenile Justice Clearinghouse, 168
    Juvenile Justice Journal, 167
juvenile statistics, 170
    Bureau of Juvenile Statistics, 167
juvenile vs. adult court
    age laws, state-to-state differences, 87, 127
    charging as an adult for violent crimes, 126-127
    charging as an adult, 21, 25, 35, 39, 48
    escape from juvenile hall or boot camp, 126
    jury vs. judge trial, 21, 48
    juvenile hall/detention center, 26
    minors and the death sentence, 153-158
    prison for youthful offenders, 26
    sentencing as juvenile, 25-26, 41, 47-48

K
Kidnapping, 115, 126

L
law enforcement site, 170
laws
    adult court, 126
    assault, 24
    burglary, 45-46
    computer fraud, 86
    conspiracy, 86
    defacement, 45
    D.U.I. 10
    D.U.I. causing injury, 136
    grand theft, 62
    habitual offender, 115
    involuntary manslaughter, 164

murder, 155
petty theft, 62
possession for sale of a controlled substance, 101
possession of alcohol in a vehicle, 10
robbery, 62
serious offenses, 115
statute of limitation, 164
storing a substance, 101
theft, 62
throwing objects, 24-25
toxic waste, 164
vandalism, 45
vehicular manslaughter, 71

legal resources, 167-180

M

Manslaughter, 115, 126. *See also* murder
involuntary manslaughter, 164-165
involuntary manslaughter, statute of
limitation, 166
murder vs. manslaughter, 166
Vehicular Manslaughter, 71-73
"meth" (methamphetamine), 94, 112
mischief, 13-26
misdemeanors, 71-73
statute of limitation, 165
Murder, 115, 119-127. *See also* Manslaughter
attempted murder, 126
definition of degrees, 156
deliberation, 155-156
judge vs. jury trial, 156
Murder, 1st Degree, and 2nd Degree, 139-158
murder vs. manslaughter, 165
premeditation, 155
statute of limitation, 165
two phases of trial, 156

N
Narcotics Anonymous, 108
National Criminal Justice Reference Service, 167
negligence, 71-73

P
parenting classes, 22
parole
       denying parole, 117
       Life Without Parole (L-WOP), 127
P.D. (Public Defender), 114
Petty Theft, 49-64
piercing, body, 107
plea agreements
       plea bargain defined, 87
       plea bargain examples, 8, 21-23, 36-37, 40-41, 55-61, 70, 84-85, 98
police resource list, 170
possession. *See* alcohol; drugs
possession of stolen goods, 63. *See also* Theft
prison, 137. *See also* boot camp; juvenile vs. adult court
       adult prison experience, 149-152
probation, failure to comply with, 110-112
probation (home), 25. *See also* electronic monitoring
probation officer (P.O.), 100
prom safety, 1-9

R
responsibility for actions, 100
restitution, 24-25, 36-38
restraining orders, 38
Robbery, 49-64, 115
       residential robbery, 115
       with personal use of firearm, 126

S
safety code. *See* laws
school resources, 169
search (rights to), shoplifting, 52-54

sentencing, 47-48. *See also* death sentence; juvenile vs. adult court
    concurrent vs. consecutive, 47
    separate sentences, 47
    turning in someone to receive a
        lesser sentence, 109
Serious and Violent Offenses, 105-118
shoplifting, 49-64, 105-107
single-parent family, 89-103
sobriety. *See* alcohol; drinking and driving
speeding, 65-73. *See also* drinking and driving
    Exhibitionist Speeding, 129
state prison, 137
statistics
    Bureau of Juvenile Statistics, 167
    juvenile statistics, 170
statutes. *See* laws
statutes of limitation, 164-166
stealing. *See* Burglary; Robbery; shoplifting; Theft
street life, 105-118
strike laws, 64, 117
    example of multiple strikes, 110, 113
    minors and the strike law, 117
    number of states having strike laws, 117
    strikes on record, 41, 55
    Third Felony Conviction, 105-118
    "third strike law" (felonies), 116
substance abuse. *See* alcohol; drugs

T
Theft, 49-64
third strike. *See* strike laws
Throwing an Object at a Vehicle, 13-26
Toxic Waste, Dumping of, 159-166
trial. *See* juvenile vs. adult court
trial as an adult, 119-127

U
urine test (alcohol), 7, 10-12

V
Vandalism, 27-48
vehicle codes. *See* laws
Vehicular Manslaughter, 71-73

W
weapons
>discharging a weapon into an inhabited
>>house, 126
>guns, 119-127, 139-158
>robbery with personal use of firearm, 126
>use of deadly weapon during felony, 115

PLEASE!!!

visit our fun and informative website

www.handcuffblues.com

You can also send mail to the author

by fax (310)652-2995

or by regular mail at:

Goofy Foot Press

P.O. Box 69365

West Hollywood, CA 90069-0365